DAWN FROM THE WEST

DAWN FROM THE WEST

The Story of Genevieve Caulfield

by MARGARET RAU

ILLUSTRATED BY DAN DICKAS

CREDO
BOOKS

Hawthorn Books, Inc.   **Publishers**

New York and London

For
Yoko Oki

CONTENTS

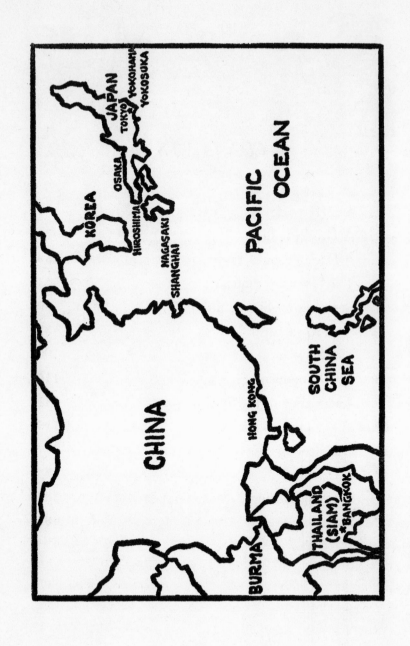

CHAPTER 1

THE TRICYCLE

"But, Mother, I *want* a tricycle," the little girl cried. "All the other children have one. Why can't I?"

Mother and daughter stood facing each other in the shimmering sunlight of that Rhode Island spring day. Everything in Pawtucket was wakening with new and joyous life. Only the little girl in her grief looked like a remnant of winter. Tears stained her cheeks and the corners of her mouth were turned down. She took a

9

long breath that was really half a sob and repeated again, "Why, Mother?"

Her mother stood looking silently at the child, not replying at once because she wanted to be sure that her voice was under control before she spoke. She was a young and lovely woman, but there was a sadness in her eyes. She yearned to drop to her knees and put her arms around her six-year-old daughter and shield her from the world. But she did not do so.

At last she spoke, and her voice was loving, but firm. All her life Genevieve Caulfield was to find comfort and inspiration in that warm, heartening voice which, though it might encourage, never tried to shelter her from facts.

"Oh, do be sensible, Genevieve," her mother said. "You know you can't see like the other children. That's why you can't have a tricycle. It would be too dangerous for you to ride it out on the road."

Then her face brightened as an idea struck her.

"But I'll tell you what we'll do," she went on, "I'll rent a tricycle for you if you promise just to ride it around in a circle in our yard. After you've had it a while, if you still want it under those conditions I'll buy one for you."

The little girl's tearful expression changed to one of joy. Her mother smiled too. She knew her daughter better than Genevieve knew herself, knew that that bright, inquiring mind and restless spirit would not be satisfied for long riding a tricycle in a circle.

She was not satisfied for long riding the tricycle.

And so it was. After a week the little girl relinquished the vehicle with a scornful gesture.

"I'm tired of it," she said. "I'd rather play at something more interesting than this."

"Something more interesting, more and more interesting!" This had been Mrs. Caulfield's motto for her daughter ever since the day almost six years before that she had learned Genevieve would never again have more than two/two hundredths of normal vision, which meant that she would only be able to distinguish light from dark.

Genevieve was just two months old when she lost her sight in the summer of 1888 in Suffolk, Virginia, where she was born. The day had started much as any other except that the doctor had come over to the house to make a routine checkup. While he was examining the baby his elbow accidentally toppled over a bottle, splattering her face with the strong medicine it contained. Her screams were warning that something terrible was happening. Then they saw her eyes and rushed her to the hospital. It was already too late.

In the weeks and months that followed, the young parents could not accept the fact that Genevieve would never see again. They hurried from specialist to specialist, but each one shook his head sadly. Each said the same thing.

"I can do nothing for her. It is a hopeless case."

Finally when Genevieve was seven months old, a young Dr. Hale of Nashville performed an operation on her right eye that permitted her to distinguish light from dark. There was no use even trying to do anything for the left eye. It had been completely destroyed.

Genevieve never heard her mother speak of the anguish she must have suffered during those dark hours when she had to face reality and make her choice. She could either give in to her mother's heart and smother her daughter with overprotection or she could give her little girl the strength of an outward going love that would help her find her own place in the world.

"Dear God," she prayed, "I want Genevieve to live a full and useful life. Help me."

Genevieve's mother followed prayer with action. As soon as the little girl could understand, she began to read to her. Sometimes her father read to her too. Then there was her father's sister, Aunt Genevieve, after whom the little girl was named and whom she always called Aunt Ducky. Aunt Ducky lived with them and not only read to Genevieve but taught her her prayers and how to cross herself and later to say the Rosary. Little Genevieve's father was a Catholic and though her mother was not, she had agreed that her children should be brought up in the Church, so she was glad to have Aunt Ducky explain her religion to the little girl.

When Genevieve was three years and eight months old, her brother Henry was born. And shortly afterwards the family moved to Pawtucket, Rhode Island, where they rented the first floor of a two-story house. Genevieve's mother encouraged her to explore the new home for herself. She did not want the little girl to become dependent on someone to lead her everywhere.

Genevieve was learning to do other things as well, to bathe and dress herself, to brush her teeth, and even to take care of her beautiful, thick brown hair. She would comb it thoroughly and then, drawing it over her shoulder, she would plait it into two firm braids which she tied with bright bows. How pretty and soft the ribbons felt under her sensitive fingers.

But Genevieve didn't stay home all day. She had two good friends. One worked with the telegraph and the other with the telephone company. Sometimes Genevieve would go to work with one or the other of these young women. Then she would spend the whole day in an office just like a grown-up. There was always something new to learn from her friends. In the telegraph office she mastered the Morse code and spent a lot of happy hours writing messages to herself on the official blanks.

Sometimes, instead, Genevieve would skip off to kindergarten with the two little daughters of the landlord. In kindergarten she would hear more stories and learn gay songs and play games. And when the other children were busy drawing or painting she would help the teacher by folding papers.

The spring that Genevieve was eight years old she went on a much longer adventure. She traveled by train with Aunt Ducky to Camden, New Jersey, to visit her grandmother. Grandmother's second husband, Mr. Hillman, was the captain of a ferry that ran between Camden and Philadelphia.

Genevieve was always welcome aboard that ferry. She would ride it for hours at a time, back and forth, back and forth. The wind would flatten itself against her face. The sun, shining from above and reflected from the waters below, would fold her in a golden warmth. All around she could hear the river murmuring in its deep, full voice, broken now and then by the throaty exclamations of the ship's whistle, while the seagulls who followed after cried and mewed plaintively overhead like lost children.

Genevieve could imagine the little ferry had broken loose from its mundane task of carrying passengers from shore to shore and was bearing them all away to far-off places.

"One day I really am going to take a long, long trip," she confided to Captain Hillman.

He only laughed and patted her head. But Genevieve was serious. She knew a great deal about distant lands because now her mother was reading geography and history to her, as well as novels like Scott's *Ivanhoe*, and poetry like Alfred Lord Tennyson's *Idylls of the King*.

Genevieve especially loved geography and history. She was fascinated with how people lived in other countries and what they had done in former days. She loved people of all kinds. Because of the reading that had been done for her, she was better educated than most children of her age. People who met her couldn't help being impressed by her inquisitive mind and bright independent spirit. She never acted as if she wanted sympathy because of her handicap. She was never heard to complain about it. In fact she had a sunnier disposition than many children.

"You ought to be proud of yourself, Frances," friends

would say to her mother. "You've done a beautiful job with Genevieve."

But Genevieve's mother would only smile, and the wistful look would come into her eyes again. She had done all she could for her little girl, but it wasn't enough. The time had come to send her away to school where she could learn the things her mother could not teach at home.

It was a difficult decision to make because in those days people didn't believe in sending young children to boarding schools. But Mrs. Caulfield had never let sentiment or custom stand in the way of doing what was best for Genevieve. And she didn't intend to now. Her real problem was to find a good school. Schools for the blind were rare then, and some of these did not have high standards. Mr. and Mrs. Caulfield made careful inquiries.

Then one day someone told them of the Perkins Institution for the Blind in South Boston. The founder of the school was Dr. Samuel Gridley Howe, the great abolitionist and husband of Julia Ward Howe who wrote "The Battle Hymn of the Republic." Dr. Howe's motto had been: "Obstacles are things to be overcome, not to be stumbled over." And his advanced methods of teaching the blind, which were demonstrated through his famous pupil Laura Dewey Bridgman, had made the school well-known.

Another pupil of his, Anne Sullivan, had become the teacher of an equally valiant blind child, Helen Keller, who had paid her first visit to the Institution the very year and month in which Genevieve was born. At that time Dr. Howe's son-in-law, Dr. Michael Anagnos, was director of the school, and he was still in charge the morning Mr. and Mrs. Caulfield and eleven-year-old Genevieve set out for South Boston and the Perkins Institution.

As soon as they stepped into the lobby of the school, Genevieve was led to a great globe of the world with all the continents embossed upon its surface.

"You can learn so many things through your fingers," Dr. Anagnos said, and he guided Genevieve's hands to the globe. Quickly her small fingers felt their way about.

"Now you're on North America, and that is South America," said the voice at her elbow as her fingers strayed. "That is Africa across the sea and now you are going northward into Europe. And here you have come to Asia!"

"Oh," Genevieve said softly. She repeated, "Oh," and then she went over the great continents for herself. She was trembling with excitement. This was almost like traveling itself.

Dr. Anagnos smiled as he told her parents that such an eager child would be a welcome pupil and that they should enroll her in the primary department which was housed in fine new buildings at Jamaica Plain.

One September morning Mr. and Mrs. Caulfield took their daughter to Jamaica Plain. All the way they listened to her gay chatter with heavy hearts, for they knew they were going to miss her and they could not help wondering if she would be homesick so far away from her family. But they kept their feelings to themselves for they did not want to spoil her happiness.

Actually there was no need to worry about Genevieve. She was always too eager to learn more and more about the world in which she lived to have time to feel lonely or left out. And there were so many wonderful new things to discover through the tips of her fingers. Always before she had had to have other people read to her. Now she would learn to read for herself. She put all her heart into it.

At that time, the line system, which consisted of raised letters, was being taught to beginners. It was much harder to learn than the English Braille system which combines raised dots to make up letters and words. There were several other systems, too, which were being taught in America. This made it very difficult for the blind since they could read only the books printed in the system they knew. Before Genevieve was out of college, however, the English Braille system was to be adopted universally, much to the relief of blind students everywhere.

During her year at school, Genevieve learned to write, too, though this was so difficult to do that she was glad in later years to exchange her pen for a typewriter over which her nimble fingers could fly without trouble. Arithmetic, music, history, poetry, handicraft, manners —they were all taught at Jamaica Plain. And study hours were pleasantly broken up with outdoor play periods.

The year went quickly by. Summer came and Genevieve returned to her home in Pawtucket full of the many wonderful experiences she had had at school. But she discovered there were exciting things going on at home, too. The family was packing again. And shortly after her return they moved to Hartford, Connecticut.

That fall Genevieve didn't go back to Jamaica Plain because there was an equally good primary school for the blind near Hartford. This school, the Connecticut School for the Blind, was so close that Genevieve could spend week ends with her family. It was much smaller than Perkins, and there was more of a family atmosphere about it.

But Genevieve spent only a year at the Connecticut School for the Blind. The next summer the Caulfield family moved again—this time to Albany, New York. Genevieve's love of travel was certainly being satisfied at an early age.

In Albany, Genevieve had a new home and yard to explore. And she and Henry had new children to become acquainted with. Henry had grown into a sturdy, lively boy, but he was always gentle and good to his sister. He took her everywhere with him, and when he made new friends he included her in the games they played. Nobody objected, because Genevieve herself was always a good sport who didn't ask for special favors. She did about as well as any of the children at games like "Ring Around the Rosie" and "Hide and Seek." Sometimes, instead, they played school, and then Genevieve was the teacher.

Whenever the children went out together, Mrs. Caulfield never forgot to caution Henry.

"Play with Genevieve just as you play with anybody else," she would say. "Only watch out for her if there's anything dangerous around. Remember she doesn't see as well as you."

Henry had ideas of his own as to how Genevieve should be protected. In every neighborhood you will find several rude children, and whenever one of these found out Genevieve couldn't see he would try to tease her by singing out, "Blind Eye! Blind Eye!"

Genevieve didn't really care. After all, she *was* blind. Her family had never tried to shield her from the fact. But gallant little Henry felt differently about it.

"Stay right where you are till I come back," he would shout over his shoulder to his sister as he dashed off. He had long sturdy legs and so he usually overtook the culprit, and when he did there was a real penalty to pay for Henry was big and strong. Before too long, no child, no matter how rude, was foolish enough to call Genevieve "Blind Eye."

CHAPTER **2**

A DREAM IS BORN

"We are moving back to Pawtucket to live with your Aunt Belle, children," Mrs. Caulfield said one day late in the second summer of their stay in Albany. "Henry can go to school there while Genevieve goes back to Perkins Primary School in Jamaica Plain."

"Oh, Mother," Genevieve exclaimed, "how wonderful!"

She loved Perkins and had missed it and all the exciting things to be learned there. Now suddenly, miraculously, she was going back. In her own joy she scarcely noticed the sadness in her mother's voice.

Mrs. Caulfield was going through troubling times, but she was keeping them to herself. She was determined her children should not know that their family, once so prosperous, was now in a precarious financial situation due to a series of wild business ventures attempted by their father. This was the reason they had to move in with Aunt Belle. Even Genevieve's schooling at Perkins would be free if they lived in New England. It was all a strict economy measure.

There was something much worse that Mrs. Caulfield wanted to keep from her children. That was her husband's growing coldness toward his family which was taking him more and more away from home. Genevieve and Henry were told only that Papa was off on business. Genevieve, who was usually so inquisitive about the whys and wherefores of such things, didn't even stop to question the reason for this sudden move to Aunt Belle's. Her mind was already far away in Perkins. She couldn't wait to get there.

She found it as wonderful as she had remembered it. Now she added music to her other studies. From the very beginning she loved those piano lessons, not minding the tediousness of scales and exercises which would enable her in the end to spin a whole new world of melody with her fingers.

Also Genevieve began to learn Braille in place of the

tedious line system. She applied herself with such a will that soon her teachers decided she was ready for the Secondary School in South Boston.

All the children at Perkins Primary School looked forward to the time when they would graduate to the Secondary School, and Genevieve was no exception. She wasn't disappointed in what she found. The school was all she had dreamed it would be. Both boys and girls attended. But they had separate classrooms and dormitories. The girls lived in five little cottages, fourteen girls to a cottage. Each cottage had its own housemother and cook. The girls did the rest of the work themselves. It was like one big family.

They took turns at the chores—waiting on tables, doing the dishes, making the beds, dusting, sweeping, and sometimes scrubbing the floors. If a girl's job wasn't done well, she could expect the housemother to call her back to do it over again. There was no use trying to get by with anything just because you were blind.

The housemother seldom had to ask Genevieve to do a job over. She enjoyed housework. But there were other things she did not like to do. She did not like to study handicrafts. The handicraft subjects were taught in a separate building, and Genevieve's feet dragged whenever it was time to go there. After a session of reading, how dull the class in knitting seemed.

Of all the handicrafts, Genevieve disliked knitting the most.

"My fingers could be used for far more important things than this," she told herself as back and forth, back and forth, her needles clicked along in her listless hands.

One day the teacher who was examining Genevieve's work shook her head.

"Genevieve," she said, "you're such a bright girl, I'm surprised at the poor job you've been doing. You've dropped a couple of stitches and you're not keeping the rows even."

"I just can't stand knitting," Genevieve answered frankly. "It seems like such a waste of time."

"It's important to learn well whatever you have to do," the teacher answered. "It's a waste of time only if you don't."

She put the knitting back in Genevieve's hands.

"Better unravel and begin again," she said.

Slowly Genevieve began to unravel her shoddy knitting. Her mind was on what the teacher had said. Suddenly up came her head in a proud little toss and out went her chin. It was the gesture she used when accepting a challenge.

"I'll show what I can do if I really put my mind to it," she said to herself.

From then on Genevieve's knitting needles clicked briskly away. The next time the teacher looked at her work she was full of praise. Genevieve had become one of the best knitters in the school.

"At least I've shown I *can* do it," she said to herself

"I'll show what I can do if put my mind to it."

with the same little toss of pride. "But I promise myself one thing. I'll never touch the silly stuff again when I leave this school and don't have to."

That time was to come sooner than Genevieve guessed. Shortly after Easter one of the girls in her cottage came down with scarlet fever. Rather than expose all the girls to the contagious disease, the school authorities sent them home. Genevieve returned to Pawtucket full of wonderful stories of her life at Perkins. In her enthusiasm, she didn't even notice her mother's strange quietness.

"I can hardly wait to get back," she concluded. "It'll only be a couple of weeks at the most they told me."

Mrs. Caulfield took her daughter's hands between her own.

"Genevieve, dear," she said, "I'm sorry, but I'm afraid it won't be possible for you to go back to Perkins. We're moving again—out of New England."

"Where, Mother?" Genevieve faltered.

"We have an invitation from Aunt Ducky and Uncle Leonard to live with them," her mother answered.

A few years previously, Aunt Ducky had married a doctor and had left the Caulfield home. Leonard Kiernan, who was a very advanced young physician, had opened one of the first sanitariums for alcoholics in the country. It was in Haverstraw, New York.

"Your Aunt Ducky's health isn't as good as it should be," Mama went on, "and they want me to come and help her take care of the place. I'd like that. I'd feel I was earning our way. It's not right to go on being a burden to Aunt Belle."

Mrs. Caulfield took a long breath. There was something more that had to be faced. Genevieve was old enough now to understand. So quickly she went on to explain that since moving to Pawtucket she had hardly seen Papa at all. She was afraid he would never come home to live with them again.

Hearing the heartbreak in her mother's voice Genevieve choked back her first rush of disappointment at not being able to return to her beloved school.

"Oh, Mother," she cried, "it will be wonderful living with Aunt Ducky again. You know how much I love her."

Haverstraw turned out to be a pleasant little town devoted to brick making and cement manufacture. Here Uncle Leonard had obtained a large house surrounded by plenty of land where a cow and some chickens could be kept. Through the portals of that house passed a steady stream of hopeless men and women from all walks of life. Writers, farmers, artists, businessmen, doctors, musicians, mechanics, old and young—they all had one thing in common. They were addicted to alcohol and had been brought by anxious relatives to be cured.

Uncle Leonard's treatment, which was far ahead of

his day, included mental as well as physical therapy. First came the physical therapy, of course. Throughout that period Dr. Kiernan kept his patients completely away from his family. After the patients were cured physically, the mental therapy began. It lasted for about a month. During that time the patients were welcomed into the family circle. Uncle Leonard felt that being accepted in this way might give them a new faith in themselves.

In the friendly home atmosphere the patients learned to relax. Sometimes they played games with Genevieve and Henry. Often they would lend a hand to the chores about the place. Genevieve also found willing volunteers to read to her so that her schooling did not really suffer. Into her eager mind were poured the contents of thick classics, and great books of all kinds. Equally as interesting were the discussions that took place among the patient-guests on subjects as varied as were their professions.

But Genevieve learned other lessons which were of even greater value, for they were spiritual. The religion her aunt and uncle practiced was not something they dragged out on Sundays. To them it was a fundamental way of life. Even their sanitarium was a labor of love.

From them Genevieve learned the true nature of service which is compounded equally of compassion and respect—respect for one's fellow being as a child of God and a brother. This was the power to heal upon

28

which Uncle Leonard relied when he invited his patients to share his home. And it worked. Into the sympathetic ears of that family circle were poured the griefs and disappointments, the guilts and remorses, and the troubles of these unhappy people. And in return they found fresh courage and a deeper insight into themselves. Most of them went back into the world to lead productive lives.

That fall Genevieve returned to school, but it was a new school, the Overbrook School for the Blind in Philadelphia. Since it was near Grandma Hillman's home she could spend her week ends there and claim her grandmother's address as her own. In this way she would not have to pay tuition which the family could still ill afford.

Genevieve found Overbrook as fine a school as Perkins. Dr. Edward E. Allen, the principal, was almost fierce in his determination that his pupils should learn to stand on their own two feet and do their share of the world's work.

"Don't think you're different from others," he liked to tell them. "Everyone has some kind of handicap. Yours is just more visible than others'. Our business in this world is to overcome those handicaps and not to use them for alibis or to capitalize on them."

But Dr. Allen didn't just lecture. He suited action to word. He encouraged, literally shoved, his students out

Genevieve found Overbrook a fine school.

into the city to travel about by themselves, either on foot or by streetcar. Once his pupils found the courage to make the plunge into complete independence they were amazed at how easy it was. They found that no matter where you went there was always someone eager to help. It was just one more proof to Genevieve that a feeling of brotherhood is natural to mankind.

She learned quickly that she could safely rely on that friendly instinct to make even longer journeys. And soon when holidays came round she was traveling alone from Philadelphia to Haverstraw and back again. It wasn't hard at all because there was always someone to help her make the two changes of train which were necessary to the trip.

Time at Overbrook passed quickly and pleasantly. In the summer of 1905, four years after her admission to the school, Genevieve was back at Haverstraw with a diploma in her hand. It was time to decide what she would do with her life. But Genevieve couldn't make up her mind. She was only seventeen, and she found it pleasant at that age just to drift along and let things happen. When the Overbrook School invited her back as a practice teacher at seven dollars a month, she accepted. Perhaps this was to be her life work, she thought.

Each one of us has a job to do on earth. Some people know from early childhood what their work is to be. It comes to others only after a long while. A few are shown the task God has earmarked for them in a flash of revelation. Genevieve was one of these.

It happened on a pleasant spring day, warm with a fragrant breeze about, a day to be outside. She was sitting on a porch swing listening to one of the teachers who was reading aloud from a magazine called *Outlook*. The teacher had turned to an article with a provocative title, "Should Japanese Children in California Be Sent to Separate Schools?"

"What a silly question," Genevieve interrupted. "Why should they?"

"Yes, it does sound foolish," the teacher agreed. "Let's see what it's about."

And she began to read aloud. The article, Genevieve quickly realized, was answering in the affirmative. She could scarcely believe her ears. A thrill of anger shot through her. She could feel it flush in her cheeks. She was hurt and embarrassed too. One of her own countrymen, a citizen of democratic America with its magnificent premise that all men are created equal, had taken the trouble to humiliate the members of another nation with that heartless article.

"Why, it's terrible," she cried out as the teacher came to the end of the article. "Do you think they would actually do such a terrible thing as discriminate against children just because they belong to a different race?"

"Oh, I'm sure it won't go that far," the teacher answered soothingly. "It's just an article."

"Just an article!" Genevieve repeated. She should have felt relieved, but she didn't. She got angrier and angrier.

Someone should show the Japanese most Americans don't feel like that, Genevieve thought. Someone, somewhere . . .

"I will show them," Genevieve said suddenly to herself. "I will go to Japan and live with the Japanese people and be their friend. I will be an example to them of the true spirit of America. That is my life's work. I know it."

Genevieve did not even stop to think of how audacious it would be for a blind girl to cross the ocean and live alone in a strange land. After all, she told herself, if she could travel from Philadelphia to Haverstraw by herself she could go to Japan too. The Japanese would be as ready to help and guide her as Americans were in this country. People were people wherever you went. But Genevieve also knew that it would be foolish to speak of her mission now to others. They would call it a foolish schoolgirl daydream and try to discourage her. She would have to work things out by herself.

The first step, of course, was to find out all she could about Japan. How could you possibly make plans to go to a country unless you knew something about it? The logical person to see was the Japanese consul. So Genevieve made inquiries and found out that there was no Japanese consul in Philadelphia. Japanese affairs were looked after by an American businessman named Franklin McFadden who hadn't even been to Japan.

Genevieve went to visit him all the same. The only piece of literature Mr. McFadden had on Japan was a Year Book. Genevieve took it back to school and with the help of volunteer readers went through it from cover to cover. She learned a great many interesting things about Japan, but the most important one to her was that they had schools for the blind.

"If they have schools for the blind, they need teachers," Genevieve said to herself. "But I'll have to have a college education to qualify. I'll have to go to college."

Genevieve had scarcely given a thought before to getting a higher education. In that day it was almost unheard of for a blind pupil to attend college. A very few boys from Overbrook had done so, but only one girl. Genevieve decided she would be the second girl. When she went home that summer she broached the subject to Mama and her aunt and uncle. Of course she didn't mention her dream of going to Japan. It was too early for that.

A wonderful thing about Genevieve's family was that they were always ready to share her enthusiasm. They all agreed at once that college was a fine idea, and they began looking into schools. Finally they settled on Trinity College in Washington, D.C.

But of course Genevieve needed preparatory work before she could even think of applying for admission there. So that September she went back to Overbrook as a pupil again. She would not only prep for college but make a serious study of music also. She didn't mind the long years of preparation that lay ahead before her life's work could begin. Her dream of going to Japan continued to shine as brightly as ever.

"Only since I'm not going to get there soon, I ought to start making Japanese friends here," she told herself.

So when someone at school mentioned that two Japanese girls were going to Women's Medical College, Genevieve went at once to look them up. It wasn't long before she was telling them about her secret. But they didn't think it strange or impossible. They were as enthusiastic about the idea as she.

During the five years she prepped at Overbrook, Genevieve kept her secret from everyone except those Japanese girls. But toward the close of her last year she let a third person in on her dream. He was a Japanese named Mr. Tadasu Yoshimoto. And he came to visit on Overbrook Day when the school held open house to show the public the work the students had done throughout the year. Mr. Yoshimoto was very interested himself in work for the blind in Japan. And Genevieve was filled with excitement when she learned he was to be a guest at Overbrook for a whole week.

"I must talk to him about my plan to go to his country," she told herself. "He will be able to advise me."

Genevieve waited all day for a chance to speak to Mr. Yoshimoto by himself. But it didn't come until that evening at the school dance. When finally she found herself alone with him she was so eager she couldn't take time to be diplomatic about it.

"Mr. Yoshimoto," she began in a burst of excitement, "I want so much to go to Japan and live and work there."

She waited, but he didn't make any reply so she just went rushing on, spilling everything out helterskelter, unburdening her heart of its dream. Still Mr. Yoshimoto said nothing. The silence lay very heavy now between them. The echo of her last words was fading forlornly in the air before he spoke.

And he hadn't caught the dream from her at all! He seemed merely perplexed at her enthusiasm. Why, he asked her, did she want to live in his country when there was, after all, a great deal more money to be made in the United States.

Money! Genevieve hadn't given a single thought to that. It didn't matter to her. Earnestly she tried to make him understand. But he still wasn't convinced. Perhaps he believed she was dreaming of a fairytale land. He began to describe the low incomes, the poor living conditions, the austerities of life in Japan that were all so different from the comforts of American living.

Genevieve listened impatiently. After all, she knew about those things from the Year Book which she could almost recite by heart.

"Mr. Yoshimoto," she told him at last, "I don't care how simply I have to live. But I sincerely want to go and work in Japan. Will you give me advice on how to prepare myself?"

Still Mr. Yoshimoto did not offer to help her. He merely said, "I'll be here at your school all week. If there is anything you wish to know about my country, please feel free to come and ask me."

Of course Mr. Yoshimoto was so astonished at Genevieve's determination to get to Japan that he immediately asked the new school principal, Mr. Burritt, all about her. From then on Genevieve's secret belonged to everyone. People inside and outside the school were ready with advice to Genevieve to forget her foolish daydream and stay home where there were plenty of ways she could be of real service.

But Genevieve didn't care now who knew about her dream or what was thought of it, because something of her eloquence must have reached Mr. Yoshimoto after all. The day he left he gave her his address which, strangely enough, was in Oxford, England.

"If you are still interested in going to Japan after two years in college, write to me and I'll help you all I can," he told her.

It was the first encouragement Genevieve had received from him and it was to shine brightly before her through the years of hard work that still lay between her and her goal.

CHAPTER **3**

A DREAM COMES TRUE

That summer of 1910 Genevieve received word she had passed her entrance examinations for Trinity College and had been awarded a scholarship there. The whole family pitched in to help her get ready for the fall event. There were clothes to be bought, of course. But most important was Genevieve's trip to the Manhattan Eye and Ear Hospital in New York for an operation to remove her worthless left eye and substitute a more natural-looking glass one.

Two or three days before the start of school, Genevieve was at Trinity College. She looked about like any other alert and eager young college woman—an attractive girl who held her head high and wore her beautiful, thick brown hair fastened in a glossy bun at the nape of her neck. Her head was very high indeed as she sat in the office of the Dean, Sister Mary.

"I don't expect special treatment," she said. "In fact, I don't want it. But since the books won't be in Braille I'll have to have students read the assignments to me. Of course, I expect to pay something. . . ."

She waited anxiously, wondering how high the fees would be for such service.

Sister Mary looked at the independent young girl sitting across the desk from her and what she saw pleased her. She laughed encouragingly as she told Genevieve not to be too hasty in her search for paid volunteers. She was sure, she explained, that with the kind of girls who came to Trinity, she wouldn't have to pay for help.

She was right. There is nothing, after all, so challenging to human beings as someone else's inspiring dream. And when the news spread that Genevieve was preparing herself for work in Japan no one could do enough to help her. The faithful volunteers who came forward to read for her never even thought of receiving pay for it.

Trinity College for Women, a younger affiliate of Catholic University, had opened in 1897 under the auspices of the Sisters of Notre Dame. Its scholastic standing was high, but because its enrollment was still small there was a warm, friendly atmosphere about it. Genevieve couldn't have found a better place to help her meet and fulfill the tough requirements of advanced education. She applied herself to her studies with a will.

But there were other important things for Genevieve to do as well. Washington was the site of the Japanese Embassy, and Genevieve soon became acquainted with some of the officials who worked there. One introduction led to another, and presently Genevieve had many Japanese friends. She discovered that there was nothing that so touched or pleased them as to learn she wished to live in their country.

The spring of Genevieve's second year in college found her as determined as ever to go to Japan. It was time to get in touch with Mr. Yoshimoto. As she sat down to write her letter she thought of the cherry trees which, a few weeks before, had been planted with due ceremony around Tidal Basin. They had come as a gift of affection from the city of Tokyo. It was one more proof to Genevieve of the feeling of kinship that exists among peoples.

"I am finishing my second year of college," she wrote. "I am still as interested as ever in going to your country and working with the blind there. I would welcome any advice and help you can give me."

The cherry trees were a gift from Tokyo.

Mr. Yoshimoto was faithful to his promise. He wrote back making many valuable suggestions. One piece of advice saddened Genevieve, but her other Japanese friends agreed that it was sound. She should, they said, graduate from a university that was known over in Japan. It would give her more prestige.

Genevieve thought about it a long while. When she went home the summer of her third year her mind was made up.

"I'm going to Teachers College at Columbia for my last year," she told her family.

"But it's so large, Genevieve," her mother remonstrated somewhat anxiously.

"It's not too large, Mama," Genevieve laughed. "After all, it's not as large as Japan. If I can't manage at Columbia University, how could I get along in Japan?"

So that fall found Genevieve in a new school, her tuition paid for by a scholarship from Overbrook. Her first day on the huge campus of Columbia University made her wonder if her mother hadn't been right after all. She felt lonelier than she ever had before. She was homesick for quiet little Trinity College. And she was afraid she might never get used to this big sprawling place with its crowds of busy, preoccupied students.

But Genevieve soon became accustomed to Columbia. She discovered that there were other students just as homesick as she. Some had come from faraway places. Cubans, East Indians, Japanese, Chinese—Genevieve met them all. Sunday nights would often find her at the Cosmopolitan Club for supper.

The year went by quickly and pleasantly. Summer came, bringing with it Genevieve's Bachelor of Science degree and her diploma from Teachers College. She had graduated from one of the largest universities in the country and was capable of earning her living anywhere teaching English. She was impatient to be on her way, but another letter from Mr. Yoshimoto had dashed these hopes.

"I advise you," he wrote, "to get a year's experience working with the blind before coming to Japan."

Another year to wait!

"Well, if it has to be done, it has to be done," Genevieve said to herself, and she went at the task cheerfully.

In the summer of 1914 she worked for the New York State Commission for the Blind, making a survey in Westchester County, and that fall returned to Perkins Institution for the Blind, this time as a teacher. The school was now located in brand new buildings in Watertown. As soon as Genevieve was settled, she wrote another letter to Mr. Yoshimoto.

"I have done survey work for the blind this summer. I am now at Perkins where I shall teach six months. I shall teach another six months at Overbrook. By summer I shall have completed all your requirements and be ready to come to Japan."

43

When the Christmas holidays arrived, Genevieve went home to Haverstraw. She showed her family Mr. Yoshimoto's most recent letters. They were, as always, friendly. They seemed to encourage, but strangely enough they outlined no definite plans, they mentioned no names and gave no details.

Genevieve wasn't worried. She was content to leave everything up to Mr. Yoshimoto. Getting to Japan was the only important thing to her. But her mother was disturbed.

"You ought to know more of what he's planning for you," she said. "It's not wise to go so far away without being informed about any of the conditions you're to work under."

Uncle Leonard and Aunt Ducky agreed. Even Genevieve's Japanese friends voiced concern about Mr. Yoshimoto's vagueness. Finally Genevieve took their advice and reluctantly sent off an inquiry to Mr. Yoshimoto. Day after day she looked for a reply. But the long months went by without an answer.

Was it the war in Europe that was causing the delay? There was a stalemate on land and Germany was trying to break it by sending out her submarines to prey on enemy and neutral shipping. On May 7, the British liner *Lusitania* was sunk without warning, carrying down with it almost two thousand people of whom over a hundred were Americans. War fever gripped the nation. President Woodrow Wilson sent a fiery protest to Germany.

That same spring, Genevieve Caulfield was stunned by her own personal catastrophe. At last she received a letter from Mr. Yoshimoto. Unlike his former friendly ones, it was cold, almost cruel. It was quite evident, he told her, that she was more interested in material gain than in helping the blind. In that case it would be wise for her to forget the whole project.

Genevieve sat in disbelieving silence as the letter was read to her. The dream which had guided her so brightly for the past five years was dead. She was bewildered and hurt. Was this God's way of showing her that she had set her sights too high, she asked herself.

Then she looked into her heart and saw that her desire to serve in Japan was stronger than ever. She did not know why she had suffered this setback. But she was not going to blame it on God's will and just give up. She straightened her shoulders, threw back her head.

"Mr. Yoshimoto or no," she said, "I'm going to Japan to live and work."

She knew she could no longer count on employment in a school for the blind in Japan, but she might be able to earn a living as an English teacher. Because it was so uncertain, however, she would have to have enough money for a return trip ticket as well as a little left over to live on while she tried to establish herself over there.

45

The only way—and a slow way indeed—to earn that money would be by tutoring foreign students in New York.

Genevieve didn't allow herself to think of how much time it would take to save enough. Back she went to Columbia University to register as a tutor. Quickly she was able to get her quota of pupils. She rented a room in a friend's apartment and, living as frugally as possible, began to bank her money.

Genevieve was now alone in the largest city in the United States, but she had already learned to find her way around in it as easily as she had in Philadelphia and Washington. Still it was a lonely life, and she often thought of Mama back in Haverstraw. Mama must be lonely, too, away from her children, because Henry also was now working in New York.

"Why don't we get an apartment together?" Genevieve suggested to her brother one day. "Then we could bring Mama to live with us."

Henry thought it was a fine idea. So a year after Genevieve had received Mr. Yoshimoto's crushing letter, the family was united again, this time in New York.

They rented a seven room apartment on Morningside Drive near Columbia University. Genevieve suggested they take in a couple of Japanese boarders. The Japanese who came to this country on business, she explained, were not allowed by their companies to bring along their wives. They had to live a lonely bachelor life

46

far from home. They would enjoy being with a family.

Henry liked the suggestion. Mama was enthusiastic about it. From then on there were always Japanese boarders in the Caulfield apartment. Genevieve learned a great deal about their country's customs from them. She practiced eating with chopsticks and sitting on the floor as the Japanese do when they gather round their low tables for a meal. She did not want to be clumsy at it when she got to Japan. She began to pick up a number of Japanese phrases and expressions too. Slowly her bank account was growing.

The years were slipping by. Henry married a lovely young girl named Beatrice Young and moved away. And presently Genevieve would be leaving too. Late in the autumn of 1922, she received a letter from one of her former boarders who had returned to Japan. He was Captain Masato Sugi of the Japanese Imperial Navy. And he was writing to tell her that for the next two years he would be stationed in Tokyo.

"Now is the time for you to come to Japan," the letter said. "You can live with us until you establish yourself. My wife and I will welcome you and do all in our power to help you."

Genevieve looked over her bank account again. Then she sold a little stock she held in the Durant Motor Company.

"I have enough, Mama," she said.

From then on everything went like magic. A young

Japanese couple who were expecting a baby were going to move in with Mama, so Genevieve wouldn't have to worry about her while she was gone.

"I'll send for you in two years if things work out, Mama," she said. "Otherwise I'll have a home to come back to."

There were any number of other things to be done before Genevieve could leave. She had to purchase a wardrobe and find substitute teachers for her pupils. She had to arrange for train and steamship passage. And of course there were always friends to be answered when they came with well-meaning advice.

"Surely you don't plan to make the long trip alone," they said. "You should try to arrange to go with someone who'll be traveling over there, too."

Genevieve only laughed.

"If I can't make a simple trip by myself," she said, "how can I dream of getting along in Japan?"

Genevieve bought a train ticket on the Northern Pacific for Seattle. Passage to Tokyo was to be on the *Iyo Maru*, a ship of the Nippon Yusen Kaisha Steamship Company. It wasn't a luxury liner. Genevieve didn't have money to waste on that. It was a cargo ship which also carried passengers.

The ship's owners charged Genevieve only half fare for her passage. A nice letter from the company told her that it was in appreciation of the great interest she had shown in Japan. Genevieve was touched. Understanding between people, she thought, was a two-way street. What you gave of good came back to you in kind.

At last the hour of leave-taking had come. It was a pleasant June day in 1923, eighteen years after Genevieve had first decided her work lay in Japan. Everyone was at the railroad station to see her off—her Japanese friends, Mama, Aunt Ducky and Uncle Leonard, Henry and Beatrice and their two little girls. Mama was the last to tell Genevieve goodbye. Then the train was moving out of the station, out of big New York, faster and faster as it gathered speed.

At the end of the railroad line Genevieve found herself in a new city—Seattle, Washington. It had been established on Puget Sound just seventy-two years before by a band of settlers from Illinois. They had traveled miles and miles over plains and mountains to reach it. It had taken them a long while to make the journey which Genevieve had completed in only a few days.

Seattle was a bustling place sprawled over seven hills and ringing Elliott Bay with piers, docks, and wharfs. Ships of many nationalities lay anchored in the bay. Genevieve's ship, the *Iyo Maru*, was among them. She found it neat and clean and smelling of new paint and engine fuel. She remembered the little ferry that, during her childhood, had carried her back and forth between

Camden and Philadelphia so many times. Now she was going on the far adventure she had so often dreamed of then. She would be two weeks at sea.

Genevieve expected to enjoy herself on the long ocean voyage. But first she had to make it plain that, once she was shown where everything was, she could get along as well as the next person. She did not want to be treated like a helpless invalid just because she happened to be blind.

As a matter of fact the *Iyo Maru* wasn't far out of port before it became apparent that Genevieve could get along better than most of the other passengers who were Americans. Since the stewards could not speak English and the Americans could not speak Japanese, there were all kinds of misunderstandings. Everything aboard ship seemed to be at sixes and sevens, and the passengers were becoming more and more irritable.

Genevieve thought she could help out by teaching the stewards a little English. She offered to tutor them. And from then on every night after dinner she conducted English classes in the empty dining hall. Presently the other passengers began to realize that Genevieve could make herself understood in Japanese, and they began asking her to interpret for them. Soon affairs aboard the *Iyo Maru* were running as smoothly as the ship's sturdy engines.

Next Genevieve took on the task of helping the radio operator translate properly the news that came over the air so the passengers would know what was going on in the world. At last even the captain came to ask her to help him with his English pronunciation. As a result, she and he had become great friends. One day he told her laughingly that he had expected to be taking care of her on the long journey and here she was taking care of his whole ship. As for the stewards, they were so grateful that on the last day aboard they expressed their gratitude by presenting Genevieve with a cake for a going away present.

Now the time had come to say farewells, for the ship was steaming into Yokohama harbor. It was a gray, rainy day. Fugiyama, Japan's great guardian mountain, was hidden behind clouds. A warm summer drizzle was dampening everything. Genevieve could not help feeling a moment of loneliness. She was far away from home, a stranger in a strange land. But as the *Iyo Maru* docked, the captain came to stand at her side.

"Your friends are waiting for you," he said. "The stewardess will see you ashore. Goodbye, Miss Caulfield."

Yes, they were there, a crowd of happy, welcoming Japanese whom she had met in New York. In the press of eager greetings, she felt a warm hand on her arm.

"I am Mrs. Sugi," a gentle voice said at her elbow. "Captain Sugi could not get away from work so I have come to take you home."

The luggage was taken care of, and Genevieve found

51

herself in a jinricksha on her way to the railway station with Mrs. Sugi. The raindrops pattered on the thick oilskin curtains which the jinricksha man had drawn to shut out the wet. The jinricksha swayed and bumped over the uneven road. But Genevieve sat very straight. She breathed in the rain-wet odors of the city, hearing the clatter of hundreds of wooden clogs along the street, the bells of vendors, the gay voices of the crowds.

How long she had worked and lived for this moment! And now it was here at last. Her dream had come true, but only because she had refused to see God's will in outer obstacles and had chosen instead to listen to the true inner voice of her heart.

CHAPTER **4**

THE GREAT EARTHQUAKE

"What a lovely house!" Genevieve Caulfield said as, following the example of her hostess, she took off her shoes and stepped over the threshold of the Sugi home.

In a Japanese style house it is the custom to remove one's shoes before entering because the fragile mats which cover the floors will not stand up under hard wear. And Mrs. Sugi's home was typically Japanese. It was built of wood so that it would roll with the land during the frequent earth tremors that visit Japan. Even the timbers were mortised rather than nailed together because nails would be shaken loose in no time.

The roof, however, was of tile. Tile roofs which overhang the wooden walls form some protection against the hazard of fire sparks. As a further precaution, many of the ridge tiles of Japanese homes are imprinted with the mask of Kahaku, the river demon, who is supposed to protect the home thus entrusted to his care.

In Tokyo, fire has been such a periodic disaster that it has come to be called the "Flowers of Edo," because Edo was the city's ancient name. Everyone is terrified when the "Flowers of Edo" burst into bloom in that city of light wooden houses.

Sliding doors and partitions covered with paper divide the interior of a Japanese house into rooms, and the latticed windows that look out on the garden are usually covered artistically with translucent paper. Every house boasts a garden, no matter how small. Sometimes it may be just a tray which contains rocks and mosses and miniature trees. But large or small the garden is landscaped to look as much as possible like some lovely natural scene.

There is very little furniture in a Japanese style home. Beds are cushions which are stored away in closets during the daytime and spread on the floor at night. People sit on the floor on cushions which, when not in use, are stacked in a corner of the room. Meals are served on a low table only eighteen inches high, around which the family kneels on cushions to eat.

The center of interest in every Japanese home is an alcove which is called a *tokonoma*. A scroll is hung at the back of the alcove. And usually flowers of the season are arranged in a vase before it. When a guest comes to dinner, he is given the seat of honor in front of this alcove but with his back to it. This was the place to which Genevieve was shown when she sat down to dinner with the Sugis that night. She picked up her chopsticks and began to eat. She still could hardly believe that she was enjoying her first meal in Japan at last.

"All your friends have been making inquiries for you about pupils who wish to learn English," Captain Sugi told her after dinner. "And we are sure we have enough now."

"But, of course, you will not start your tutoring until September," Mrs. Sugi added. "Nobody will want to begin anything as difficult as the study of English until the summer weather is over. Meanwhile, make yourself at home with us."

Summer weather in Japan is hot and humid. It is particularly unpleasant during the rainy season which lasts from one month to six weeks, beginning about the middle of June. During that time, the sun seldom shines. A continuous drizzle saturates the earth. All through the gray summer days the cicadas trill in sharp high voices. The night is heavy with the croaking of frogs. And everyone does as little work as possible. But Genevieve never thought of letting a little hot weather stop her from visiting old friends and getting acquainted with the great city of Tokyo.

The central area of the city is built in a basin of low, marshy land along either bank of the Sumida River. Here is the glittering Ginza Way, most famous shopping street of Tokyo. Here are the Imperial Palace grounds, several large parks and amusement centers, and crowded residential districts. Extensive suburbs spill out over the high ground to the west of downtown Tokyo, and the Sugis lived in one of these.

Unlike New York City, which is set out in symmetrical blocks, Tokyo sprawls in all directions. Its streets are narrow and winding, and its numbers are confusing. Genevieve would have been hopelessly lost if it had not been for the clever and courteous jinricksha men who knew Tokyo inside out and could find any address no matter how hidden.

She found Tokyo a lively city indeed. The sharp staccato clatter of hundreds of clogs reverberated with especial emphasis on the wooden pavements of streets like the Ginza. The tinkle of vendors' bells and the cries of peddlers sounded everywhere.

"*Kingyo! Kingyo!*" sang the goldfish peddler among his bowls of gleaming fish.

She found Tokyo a lively city indeed.

"*Hotaru! Hotaru!*" chanted the firefly peddler from the midst of small gauze-covered cages in which fireflies crept about waiting for the night to start flicking their lights.

The peddlers of singing insects who carried their wares in tiny bamboo cages swinging jauntily from poles over their shoulders had no need to call out anything. The singing insects took care of that, filling the air with their clear trills.

There were many food stalls where people could stop for a quick snack. But Genevieve had no need of them. Wherever she went calling, she could always count on being served anything from tea to a full meal. You cannot step over the threshold of a Japanese home without being offered something to eat. That is Japanese etiquette.

"For every new dish you try, your life will be prolonged seventy-five days," a Japanese saying goes.

August went swiftly by. On one bright, windy day, the women of Tokyo brought out all their folded clothes and aired them to kill fungi and insect eggs deposited during the rainy season. For several days, the households were completely disrupted by lines of fluttering kimonos hung from ropes that crisscrossed all the rooms and the garden as well.

This was the sure sign of fall. Soon it would be time for Genevieve to begin her tutoring. Her principal pupil was to be Mr. Nakamura, a wealthy businessman who lived in Yokohama. Genevieve was to make the pleasant trip to the nearby city every Friday. She would stay at Mr. Nakamura's home Friday night and tutor the whole family. She would spend Saturday morning at his office handling his English correspondence. At noon, she would return to Tokyo again.

The first lesson was set for August 31. But, at the last minute, Mr. Nakamura decided to postpone it until the following Friday, because the thirty-first was a national holiday. This gave Genevieve one more week end of freedom, and she decided to spend it with Mrs. Sekikawa, an old friend she had known in New York.

Mrs. Sekikawa, whose husband had remained in the United States, had just returned to Japan. She lived in another suburb of Tokyo, and it took Genevieve an hour by jinricksha to reach her home.

Mrs. Sekikawa greeted her warmly. She had so much to tell Genevieve about Mama and Henry and his wife and their little daughters and many other friends as well. It was very late before the two women even thought of going to bed.

The air was hot and humid, smelling of typhoon. Mrs. Sekikawa looked worried. September 1 in Japanese tradition has always been an unlucky day. It was believed that if there was a typhoon on this day there would be typhoons throughout the month.

"If it comes, it will destroy the rice crop that is just now ripening," Mrs. Sekikawa explained. "Everyone will suffer. I hope it passes us by."

But Mrs. Sekikawa's hopes went unheeded. Genevieve woke to the sound of a howling wind and torrential downpour. Somewhere to the north a typhoon had struck, and Tokyo lay in its outer perimeter. There was no use trying to brave that weather. Genevieve could only wait until it cleared. It was eleven-thirty before the sun blazed out again.

"You might as well stay for lunch now," Mrs. Sekikawa decided.

So Genevieve was still at Mrs. Sekikawa's house

when, at two minutes to twelve, a strange tremor suddenly ran through the house. Then it began to roll just as the *Iyo Maru* had rolled at sea. Only this was on land.

"What's wrong?" Genevieve asked, bewildered.

Mrs. Sekikawa caught her breath sharply.

"Earthquake!" she said.

Quickly the rolling movement gathered intensity. It seemed as though the house had been seized in the jaws of a great animal and was being shaken violently. The two women could not even stand upright. All about them, dishes were smashing to the floor. Pots and pans were clattering wildly. Cushions, flower vases, books— everything movable was flying about. It seemed as though the battered, wrenching house must split apart. But it did not. It continued to roll with the undulating earth. Only the roof tiles were dislodged and could be heard clattering to the ground outside.

Presently the first shock faded in intensity. It had seemed like an eternity though it had really lasted only five minutes. But the earth continued to quiver threateningly at intervals. Mrs. Sekikawa and Genevieve, trembling, started for the door.

Outside the street was littered with tiles. A thin, yellow-gray dust was hanging over everything. And people were running to and fro shouting and crying.

"Earthquake! Earthquake! Earthquake!" could be heard on all sides.

Now, from the central part of the city, dull explosions began to sound at intervals. Oil storage tanks and gas mains, cracked open by the quake, were exploding.

"Fire! Fire!" a new cry went up. And everyone stared in horror toward downtown Tokyo. Here and there columns of smoke could be seen rising into the hot, sunny air.

The quake had struck at the noon hour when, in private residences and restaurants alike, fires had been started for the midday meal. People had been too terrified to think of anything other than fleeing their houses, leaving the live charcoals in their lighted *habachis* to be flung about over the inflammable floor mats. The terrible "Flowers of Edo" were beginning to bloom again.

As the people in the upland suburbs watched, the individual fires spread rapidly. They were helped by the light afternoon breeze that was now blowing in from the sea. It carried sparks from burning houses to the tinder dry framework of others from which the protective tiles had been ripped. It cast other sparks on refugees clogging the narrow streets with cartloads of inflammable household belongings. Soon the packed streets became blazing rivers of fire. Still other sparks set fire to the household goods of refugees helplessly packed on the wooden bridges that spanned the Sumida River. Bridges and refugees went up in flame together.

As the afternoon breeze grew in intensity, more and more sections of the city caught fire. Now a wide area of central Tokyo was an ocean of lurid flame that rolled in surges under a black pall of smoke. It was hard for the people in the suburbs to believe that living people were down there frantically seeking some place of safety.

Suddenly, in the sky above the fire, a cloud appeared like a great winged angel.

The terrible "Flowers of Edo" were blooming.

"Rain, rain," Mrs. Sekikawa cried hopefully.

"Oh, thank God for rain," Genevieve echoed thankfully.

"Rain," the neighbors took up the cry and all pointed at the white cloud hopefully.

But it was not rain. The cloud had been formed only by the heat of the fire striking the cooler air above. Tortured by the upward draft of heat, it was sending back miniature tornadoes, "dragon twists" as they were called by the Japanese. These whirling, black dervishes of wind which were composed of deadly carbon monoxide gas caught up flaming debris when they passed through burning areas and scattered it far and wide.

At four o'clock, the largest of the dragon twists whirled across the Sumida River and advanced upon a wide, open space known as the Union Depot. Here forty thousand refugees had gathered for safety. Many had brought bedding and were preparing places to sleep for the night, congratulating themselves upon escaping the worst of it.

With a horrible, roaring sound the twister made its way across the wide space. It rolled and tumbled people about like so many peas, set fire to the bedding here and there, and then passed on. In its wake only a few hundred people were left alive. Those who were not burned to death had been asphyxiated by the carbon monoxide gas.

There were no fires in Mrs. Sekikawa's residential section, but there was anguish of a different sort. Many of the neighborhood men had gone to work that morning in downtown Tokyo. What had become of them? There was no way even of trying to reach their places of business by telephone. All the lines were down. The telegraph office was out of commission too. Genevieve could not send a cable to her mother to tell her she was all right.

By evening, the earth was still shaking. Everyone was sure another quake even bigger than the last would strike. Mrs. Sekikawa thought the safest place to sleep that night was in the garden. With the help of her two children, she brought out the wooden winter shutters. Bed cushions and coverings were spread upon them, and big mosquito nets were stretched over them.

A neighbor woman who had just moved into the locality and had as yet not even met Mrs. Sekikawa came hurrying over.

"I noticed you have a foreigner staying with you," she said. "It must be very uncomfortable for her to have to sleep on the shutters. I have an American bed I'd be very glad to lend her."

The woman's voice was anxious. It was obvious she was deeply worried, perhaps over someone down in the city. Yet she had been considerate enough to think of making a stranger comfortable.

But there are no strangers in times of catastrophe, Genevieve thought in surprise. We are all related then.

She thanked the woman warmly, but she did not want the bed. She lay down on the shutters beside Mrs. Sekikawa and her two children.

The wind that had been blowing off the sea all day

now veered as was its custom and began to blow steadily from the land. This brought the fire to buildings as yet unharmed. In the dark night, the flames, reflected on the clouds above, seemed to tower into the heavens. An acrid burning odor filled the air. The earth continued to quiver.

Genevieve thought of her mother and brother so far away. She thought of her childhood, of the long years that had followed her decision to come to Japan, the strong sense of mission. Was it all to end in this—earthquake and fire and who knew what fresh disaster? She tried to pray, but she could find no comfort in her prayer. Where was God? He seemed to have deserted His world.

Just then Mrs. Sekikawa's small son cried out, "There's the moon."

"Yes," Mrs. Sekikawa echoed wonderingly, "it's coming up. It's shining."

The late full moon had indeed risen. It hung in the sky, serene, untouched, looking down as though with compassion upon the tortured city below.

"The moon," Genevieve whispered.

It seemed to her a symbol of God's love, ever faithful, promising an abiding peace beyond the chaos that tortured the moment. That was what was important—that He was always there—and not whether she lived or died. How could she ever have doubted Him?

"Yes," she whispered, "God is in His Heaven, and He cares for His people, no matter what happens."

By Sunday, most of the neighborhood men who had escaped central Tokyo had straggled home. Some would never come back.

As the day progressed, refugees from the city began to swarm through the suburbs. Few had had anything to eat since the previous day. Their faces were grimed and weary and filled with the horror of what they had seen and suffered.

What could one do for so many? Mrs. Sekikawa didn't stop to ask that question. She had some rice in the kitchen and that meant she could do something. She and Genevieve cooked the rice and made it into balls, placing a plum in the center of each. They went back out to the street and began to hand the balls to the refugees as they came by.

All day long Tokyo continued to burn. The panic which had overcome the people made it easy for them to believe the senseless rumor that the fires were being started by disgruntled Korean immigrants. Bands of young hoodlums armed with improvised weapons went out to hunt down the unfortunate Koreans. Some Japanese who were mistaken for Koreans were killed also. It was the darkest, most terrible hour of the whole catastrophe for it showed the ugly depths into which hate and suspicion can plunge men.

Finally, early Monday morning, brave city firemen at

a loss of some twenty lives subdued the blaze. Martial law, combined with the good sense of the Japanese, put an end to vicious vigilante groups.

By Wednesday, Genevieve was able to return to Mrs. Sugi's home where she was warmly greeted by her anxious friend. Mrs. Sugi's only worry now was over her husband's safety. Mr. Sugi, who had recently been promoted to a rear admiral, was stationed at the great naval base of Yokosuka which had also been hard hit. No word had come through from him as yet, and all that was known were the vague rumors of disaster that were floating about everywhere.

In the days that followed, Genevieve learned the true loyalty of her Japanese friends. They came by jinricksha or on foot to inquire about her. One walked all the way across the fire-scorched, debris-littered city to give her a piece of comforting news.

"I'm going to Kobe," he told her. "And I wanted you to know I plan to cable your mother from there that you're safe and well."

The disaster that had befallen Japan was the worst in modern history. It had struck a wide area including the coastal regions around Sagami Bay and Tokyo Bay. Tidal waves had poured in along the Sagami coastline. The towns around Tokyo Bay, where there were no tidal waves, had burned to the ground, but most of the inhabitants had managed to escape.

The worst hit cities were Yokohama and Tokyo.

Eighty per cent of Yokohama was destroyed. Sixty per cent of Tokyo had burned to the ground, and a hundred thousand of its inhabitants had been killed. Over one hundred and fifty thousand were seriously injured. More than a million and a half were homeless. Water pipes had burst, creating a shortage of water. For a week the city of Tokyo had little more in the way of food than some raw fish, pears, and unpolished rice. Yokohama was in even worse straits.

Both cities set to work with a will to bring order out of chaos. But aid was also on its way from the outside world. The first on the scene were the ships of the United States Asiatic Fleet. As soon as the news of the disaster was broadcast, they sailed from as far away as Manila bringing all the supplies they could carry.

The International Red Cross quickly began gathering relief funds too. On the very afternoon of September 1, President Coolidge asked the people of the United States to contribute five million dollars to this fund. But Americans, appalled by the tragedy, subscribed more than one hundred per cent above the amount asked of them.

Genevieve was proud of her country's response, but it was not enough for her to rest on the merits of others. She wanted to do her share.

"How can I help?" she asked Mrs. Sugi.

"Cold weather will soon be here, and many people have only their light cotton summer kimonos," Mrs.

Sugi replied. "Most of the clothing stores have burned down. But there are some wool shops left. People who can knit are being asked to make the yarn into warm clothes for the refugees. Can you knit by any chance?"

Genevieve smiled. She was remembering her words back in the handicraft class at Perkins: "When I leave this place, I'll never touch the silly stuff again."

She never had either, not in college or since. But here in ravaged, suffering Tokyo the lowly skill of knitting had taken on a great importance. It could keep people well. It would prevent babies from dying of cold.

"Bring me the wool; I can knit," she told Mrs. Sugi.

Genevieve Caulfield knit with a will. She knit from early morning until late at night. Her fingers became first sore and then calloused. Scarves, sweaters, baby jackets, one after the other they slid out from her swiftly moving needles. How many she didn't know. She didn't bother to count. As soon as she finished one, she just began on the next. And with every stitch she spoke a prayer of gratitude for the teacher who had insisted she learn a lowly skill she didn't like.

CHAPTER 5

LET YOUR LIGHT SO SHINE

"GENEVIEVE, BEST COME HOME AT ONCE," the telegram read.

It was from Mama, and Genevieve received it as soon as Tokyo resumed communications with the outside world. She held it in her hand a long while, picturing the apartment at home—Mama frantic with worry, Henry and Beatrice trying to console her, but anxious themselves. She did not like to cause worry to her family. What should she do?

70

Many of her Japanese friends were counseling her to go home also. Hard times, they told her, would surely follow on the heels of this terrible natural disaster. Living conditions would drop. There might even be a business panic. Who would be interested in studying English under such conditions?

Genevieve had to admit there was reason to their argument. All her prospective pupils had evaporated. Some were dead. Others felt they could no longer afford the luxury of English lessons. Mr. Nakamura, who was to have been her chief source of income, had been killed by a tile while walking the street the day the earthquake struck.

Once more Genevieve turned from the outside obstacles to look into her heart. After all she had been through, did she really want to stay on, she asked herself.

The answer was that she did. There was no lessening of her love for Japan. The only thing that troubled her was the thought that she might not be able to find work and would become a burden to her friends. She was used to taking things to God so she asked Him to guide her in the difficult decision she must make. Her mind felt freer then.

"I will wait until Admiral Sugi comes home and ask his advice," she told herself. "He has so much common sense, I will do what he says."

At all events, she couldn't think of leaving Mrs. Sugi now. They were cruel days for her friend who had to face the possibility that her husband might not return at all. Yokosuka had been much closer to the center of the earthquake than either Yokohama or Tokyo. And since it was a great naval base it had contained huge storage tanks filled with enough oil to supply the Japanese fleet for two years. These had burst apart in the quake and then ignited, flowing down into the harbor in great swathes of flame. What the earthquake had not destroyed in Yokosuka was burned to the ground.

A whole week went by before Mrs. Sugi received any word from her husband. Then it came by a messenger who arrived on foot at the Sugi home to tell her that the admiral was safe but too busy to come home. It was still another week before he could get away to visit his family in Tokyo.

When he came, Genevieve took her problem to him. But Admiral Sugi only smiled at her fear of being a burden to her Japanese friends. He told her that if she didn't mind the uncertainty of the days ahead she should stay. She would be welcome in his home for as long as she chose to live there.

God had answered her prayer.

Now, thought Genevieve, the rest is up to me.

She firmly believed that Heaven helps best those who help themselves first. So she began going over the list of all the people she had met in New York while she had been working to earn money to come to Japan.

Suddenly two people came to mind. One was an American named Caroline MacDonald. She had come to Tokyo to open a settlement house for working people.

Perhaps I can be of use to her, Genevieve thought.

The other was a Japanese named Mr. Choshichi Ito. He was the principal of the Tokyo Prefectural Fifth Middle School for boys.

"If you really do come to my country," he had told her in New York where he had been visiting, "I want you to teach English at my school."

At the time Genevieve hadn't paid much attention to his invitation because she had much preferred private tutoring. Now she gave him a telephone call.

Within a half hour of Genevieve's call, Mr. Ito was at the Sugi home to offer her a full-time teaching job. But Genevieve wanted more freedom, so she agreed to teach only two days a week. She would have four classes with fifty boys in each.

Shortly afterwards, Miss MacDonald also came to ask Genevieve to teach English one night a week in the night school she was starting at her settlement house. Once more Genevieve had a basic income to which she could add with private tutoring. Finally she found a new home with a wealthy Japanese family. In return for her room and board, she would tutor the children in English. This move would free Mrs. Sugi to accompany her husband to Yokosuka.

All the boys in the Fifth Middle School had heard of their new teacher. The first day of the first class fifty heads turned as Genevieve walked to the front of the room. Whether she stayed on or not depended on how well she could manage this class of thirteen-year-old boys. Mr. Ito had offered her an assistant to help keep order, but Genevieve had declined. If she couldn't handle the boys by herself, she explained, she shouldn't be teaching at all.

And now as she faced the class she realized that she was not the only one on trial. If she succeeded, it would make it easier for other blind people in Japan to get teaching jobs. The thought that so much depended on her made her a little nervous. She began with a calm she didn't feel by asking the boys for their names. One by one she wrote them down in Braille in her notebook. She knew the boys were watching her curiously. There was a deep silence in the room.

Finally roll call was over. Genevieve put down her book and rose to her feet. A buzz went through the class room and then died away as she began to speak.

"It's quite clear to me that boys love to play and try to take advantage of the teacher," she said pleasantly. "I used to like to do it too. But there's not much reason in trying to take advantage of me. It's too easy. So I think it might be a good idea for you to study instead."

The boys looked at one another. They had been put on their honor. That took all the fun out of playing pranks.

Genevieve's other teaching assignment took her to

74

Miss MacDonald's settlement house, a quiet, dignified building in a good section of town. Here the labor union members could gather, hold meetings, study, and attend lectures.

But because Miss MacDonald had worked with prisoners in America, she wasn't content to confine her work to labor union affairs. She spent many hours visiting men in prison also. When they were released, she invited them to stay at the settlement house until she could find work for them. This was often difficult because everything of importance that happened to a man was entered on his family registration card. And no employer would think of hiring him without first seeing the card.

In her free time, Genevieve often went with her friend to visit the men in prison. They were grateful for her sympathy and poured out their hearts to her. Genevieve had learned how to give encouragement and comfort from her days in Uncle Leonard's sanitarium in Haverstraw. She realized then that all experience can be put to good account if one is willing to accept it and learn from it. She came away from the Japanese prisons with the words of the Master ringing in her ears:

"I was in prison, and you came to me." She tried to look for Him in all the downtrodden and lost ones of the world.

Sometimes she could help by teaching the men special skills when they were paroled from prison. One of these men was a totally deaf army officer. She taught him typing. Then she took him to a day school where he could learn lip reading. Because of her help he was able to get employment, but he was soon in trouble again. This time he was sent to the most formidable prison in all Japan.

Genevieve was sad to see him throw away his life. But she did not allow herself to be discouraged. She was convinced that any act of true compassion will bear its fruit in time.

Two days at the Fifth Prefectural School and one night teaching English at Miss MacDonald's settlement house left Genevieve a great deal of time to herself, and she quickly filled it with private pupils. By the time she was well into her second year in Japan, she knew her period of probation was over. She had proved she could not only support herself comfortably but could take care of her mother as well. It was time to send for Mama.

But, of course, she would not want to bring her mother to a room in someone else's house. They would need a place of their own, so Genevieve went house-hunting. At last, she found a two-story house halfway up a hill in the Mita residential district. A tram stop was located conveniently at the base of the hill. There was a Shinto shrine, a small Buddhist temple, and a tiny ink factory nearby. A marquis lived on top of the hill. The neighbors were all pleasant and friendly.

Genevieve rented the house and hired a maid. She sent for her piano too. She had been without it for two years, and she had missed it very much. It was like a dear old friend to her. Then at last on a fine October day she went down to Yokohama to meet the ship that was bringing Mama to Japan.

Genevieve had been so busy getting things ready that she hadn't stopped to ask herself whether her mother would really like Japan. Now she remembered that Mama would be far away from home and brother Henry and his family. What if she was unhappy here in this strange land? It wouldn't be an easy thing to send her home again. Genevieve was filled with anxiety. But she need not have worried. Mama came hurrying down the gangplank of her ship and put her arms around Genevieve.

"Oh, I'm so glad to be here at last," she said, and Genevieve knew that everything was going to be all right.

And so it was. Mama loved the house. She loved Tokyo. It wasn't a strange city to her after all. She found many old friends whom she had known in New York. Soon it was as though she had always lived in Japan.

Genevieve was happy. She and Mama were now reunited in a home of their own in the country of which she had dreamed for so long. Still something was lacking.

Her name was Haruko which means Spring Child.

"Mama, a home needs a child to make it complete," she said. "I'm going to adopt a little girl."

So she began looking around for the daughter she wanted so much to have. Then one day a friend told her of just the right child. She was fourteen years old, and her name was Haruko, which means Spring Child. She was the middle one of eleven children. Her grandfather had been a wealthy and respected citizen in a little town outside Tokyo. But when he died, his son, Haruko's father, had squandered all the wealth he had inherited and had come to Tokyo to live. Haruko's mother had died years before. Her father had remarried and neither he nor her stepmother loved the little girl. They were glad to give her up to Genevieve.

Haruko was a very unhappy child when she first came to live at the Caulfield home. She was small for her age. But she was as honest and dependable as an adult. And she was hungry for love. Genevieve and Mama took the little girl to their hearts, and Haruko responded eagerly. All that was in her of beauty and trust came rushing out to return the affection her new family lavished upon her.

One day Haruko said to Genevieve, "Mama, I would like to become a Catholic."

Haruko had often accompanied Genevieve to church and Genevieve had explained something of her religion to the little girl. But she had never urged her to join the Church. Though it would have been nice to have

Haruko do something just to please her, Genevieve wanted her new daughter to be sincere in her religion.

So there was no happier mother in the world than Genevieve when, after taking instruction, Haruko was baptized into the Catholic Church. Now the little family was truly united, because her own mother, impressed by the strength her daughter had found in her faith, had become a Catholic also.

Genevieve's adopted family did not stop with Haruko. It was the custom in Japan for the district police to make a monthly check on the occupants of every house in the district. The policeman who came calling at the Caulfield home was young and polite. Genevieve, who was always curious about everyone she met, asked him all about himself. He told her he was going to night school to study law because he had to pass an examination to get promoted.

"I have to know English," he said. "But it is really a difficult language to learn."

"I'll be glad to help you with it," Genevieve offered.

"I'd like to take lessons from you, Miss Caulfield," the policeman replied unhappily, "but I just can't afford it."

"I'll *give* you an hour of tutoring if you come in the early morning before my regular students," Genevieve suggested, impressed by the young man's eagerness.

The policeman accepted her generous offer gratefully. Presently he was bringing fellow members of the police force to his "English class." Then the superior officers showed up too. They were all intensely interested in learning English. Genevieve set aside a spare room in her house for a study room which they could use any time they were off duty. From then on, policemen could be seen going in and out of the Caulfield home at odd hours all through the day.

"It's the branch of the Mita Police Station," the neighbors liked to joke. But there was respect in their voices. It was nice to have policemen for friends.

CHAPTER 6

FEED MY LAMBS

"Will you help my men?" Dr. Muto asked Genevieve one day late in 1932. "They've lost all interest in life. If anyone can give them hope, it's you."

Dr. Muto, a general in the medical corps of the Japanese army, had been Genevieve's private pupil for years and had come to admire her deeply. The men he was speaking of were ten soldiers who had been blinded dur-

82

ing the Japanese invasion of Manchuria. They were now leading a listless existence in a ward of his hospital, all hopes for the future cut short by what they imagined was an insurmountable handicap.

"Of course, I'll try," Genevieve said eagerly.

She did not stop to remind herself that the soldiers had been wounded during a war of aggression which the Japanese army had started in the fall of 1931. To her, they were just unfortunate young men who had followed without question the orders of their superiors and were now in need of help. And she was grateful to Dr. Muto for giving her the first opportunity she had had in Japan to work with the blind. This was because schools for the blind were progressive and well-staffed and she had long since discovered that her help was not needed.

Taking along a Japanese Braille newspaper, she went to see the young men. She found them huddled forlornly together in their ward.

"Why are you so gloomy?" she asked them cheerfully.

"What is there to live for?" one of them replied in a dispirited voice.

The others echoed his question.

"Nonsense," Genevieve told them. "You can still be useful. You can learn many things through your fingers. Reading, for instance. I'll show you."

She picked up the Braille newspaper and, running her

fingers lightly over the raised perforations in it, she read aloud.

"It isn't possible," one of the men exclaimed.

"You're only joking," several others remonstrated accusingly.

Genevieve let them pass their own fingers over the paper to feel the raised dots. Then she had them place

She spelled out the passages.

their hands on her swiftly moving fingers as she spelled out the passages. The astonishment of the young men changed to hope, and this grew to earnest determination.

Two hours, two afternoons a week, for two years,

Genevieve taught the young men. She watched them change from apathy to enthusiasm. Eagerly they worked to bring themselves back to the world they thought they had lost.

Genevieve was happy for them, but her mind was troubled those days by a different and far more ominous kind of blindness that was deepening over Japan. It was the blindness of the military clique that was rapidly driving the nation to disaster.

Back in 1926, when Emperor Taisho had died and his son, the Regent Hirohito, had ascended the throne, it had looked as though a new era was dawning for Japan. Emperor Hirohito took the title of Showa for his reign. *Showa* means "Enlightened Peace," and the young Emperor was truly sincere about his twin aims of peace abroad and a liberal government at home.

But he was young and vulnerable, and the military men in Japan were well entrenched and powerful. While maintaining loyalty to the Emperor, they did as they pleased without even consulting him. They were able to gain still more power when the world depression struck Japan in 1930. Then people were so desperate they were ready to accept without question any regime that promised them help.

As the thirties progressed, more and more societies dedicated to achieving ultranationalist aims through violence sprang up. Assassinations of liberal men in important government posts became frequent. The loyalty of liberal people outside the government began to be questioned. Some were even jailed. The Emperor himself was severely criticized for continuing his interest in scientific studies.

In the schools, more and more time was given to a study of Shinto mythology with especial emphasis on the superiority of the Japanese race. And there were longer hours of more arduous military training for the young pupils.

A new brand of policeman appeared on the streets of Tokyo. He was a member of the Kem Petai, the military police force. Unlike the pleasant civilian policemen of the Mita police station, the men of the Kem Petai spent their time investigating alleged subversion. One day one of them even called on Genevieve to cross-examine her about her work with the ten blind soldiers, as though it had been a crime.

Genevieve discovered that her friends, too, were being subjected to questions by the Kem Petai. Suddenly, just knowing her or any foreigner had become almost a sin of disloyalty in the eyes of ultranationalistic Japanese. Today the Japanese often refer to those years between 1931 and 1941 as "the dark valley."

At last Genevieve realized sadly that she could no longer go on working in this strangling atmosphere. She and her family would have to leave Japan. What should she do? She could, of course, return to the United States where work could always be found. But she did not

want to leave the Orient. It seemed to her that somewhere out here there was a task just waiting for her. She
prayed to God to guide her to that place.

Then one day Father Eylenbosch of Sophia University, a Jesuit school in Tokyo, introduced her to a
young Siamese student. Genevieve had never lost her
curiosity in geography. She asked the young man about
his country.

The more he told her of Siam, which today is known
as Thailand, the more Genevieve was intrigued. In all
Southeast Asia, Thailand alone had withstood coloniza-
tion by the big European powers. Its kings had been
absolute monarchs, but most of them had governed
wisely. The most recent one, King Prajadhipok, had
abdicated in 1935 in favor of a constitutional government. His young nephew, Ananda Mahidol, had been
crowned king in a role similar to that of the English
monarch.

As the days went by, the young student introduced
Genevieve to other Thais, and eventually she came to
know the Thai minister himself.

"What are you doing for the blind in your country?"
Genevieve asked all her new friends.

They laughed good-humoredly. They had never
heard of any blind people there they told her.

Finally Genevieve met a young Thai doctor, Dr.
Fonthong Saengsingkaeo. Dr. Fonthong did not laugh
at Genevieve's question.

"Of course there are many blind people—both children and adults—at home," he told her gravely. "So far as I know, nothing has been done for them at all."

Then, early in 1936, Genevieve met a very important Thai who had come to Tokyo for a visit. He was Luang Pradit Manutram, the Minister of the Interior in Thailand's new government. Luang Pradit was enthusiastic about Genevieve's desire to help the blind in his country. But he suggested that she pay a visit there first to see if she liked it. If she did, he would do everything in his power to help her, he promised.

Genevieve was elated. During the rest of that school year, she spent her spare time transcribing the Thai alphabet into Braille. It is the first step necessary to starting a school for the blind in any country. With an alphabet, Braille textbooks can easily be prepared.

When the Tokyo prefectural schools had dismissed for summer vacation, Genevieve and Haruko left Mama behind with friends and went to see what it was like in Bangkok. They traveled by ship, the air growing warmer and more tropical with every mile southward. In ten days they reached the mouth of the Chao Phraya River on which, about twenty miles upstream, stands Bangkok, the capital of Thailand.

The muddy river swarmed with small boats on their way to the city with produce to sell. The exotic scent of strange, rich fruits and vegetables filled the air with fragrance. On all sides rose the gay voices of the people on the boats and the laughter of children who were swimming and splashing about in the water. The Thais are a carefree race.

Genevieve found Bangkok a crowded city, so intersected with canals that it is sometimes referred to as the Venice of the East. Even Japan in the summer could not compare with the heat of tropical Bangkok. But the crowds that thronged the narrow streets did not seem to mind. They went about their business on foot, by pedicab or bus, in clothes as gay as their voices.

Dr. Fonthong had already returned to Thailand, and he met Genevieve at the pier. Luang Pradit was also back. Now he was Minister of Finance. He seemed as enthusiastic as ever about Genevieve's school. But, at the time, he was preoccupied with nursing his ill father, and it was Dr. Fonthong who took Genevieve around to meet the other cabinet members.

Not one of them showed interest in Genevieve's project.

"It would be easier to teach tables and chairs than to teach the blind anything," some told her.

"It will cost too much," others said.

It was useless for Genevieve to try to explain that, with willing hearts, a school for the blind could be easily run on a shoestring. She and Haruko had to return to Japan without any encouragement at all.

"Mama," said Haruko on the way back, "what are your plans now?"

89

"Plans?" Genevieve laughed. "Why, to start a school for the blind in Bangkok, Haruko."

"But, Mama, no one thinks it can be done," Haruko cried.

"Then it's all the more important for us to show them how," Genevieve replied.

As soon as she got back to Japan, Genevieve began planning to return to the United States. Haruko, who was now a young lady in her twenties, was to go along too. Genevieve was very proud of her daughter. Haruko had a fine artistic talent, and Genevieve had arranged for her to study under a French modiste in one of Tokyo's department stores. Haruko could not become a United States citizen because of the Oriental Exclusion Act. But if she wished, after her visit in America, she could return to Japan and make a name for herself as a dress designer.

As for Genevieve, she meant to spend her time in America giving lectures to raise money for her work in Bangkok. But there was something more important to her than just making money. Most of the people in Japan were peace-loving and wanted no part of the militaristic clique which had come into power.

If only I could do my part to bring sincere people of both countries together, Genevieve thought, it might help.

She knew she was just one person and that whatever she said or did would be just a drop in the bucket. But she knew, too, that God judges not by outer achievements but by the sincerity that motivates each heart.

February of 1937 was the date Genevieve set to leave Japan. It would give the family six months to wind up all their affairs. Much had to be done. In the thirteen years Genevieve had lived here, she had accumulated many things. She began giving away her furniture and most of her other possessions to friends. She gave notice to her kindly landlord. She began to let her pupils know that they would have to find other teachers. It was a sad business.

The time grew shorter and shorter. Presently the New Year season came round. The Japanese celebrate their New Year on January 1 as does the Western world; however, in Japan it lasts several days and is the most joyous season of their calendar. But there was more sadness than joy in the hearts of Genevieve and her friends as they celebrated the holiday together for the last time.

Too soon the happy days were over. January passed and February arrived. The time of parting had come at last.

On a cold day in mid-February, the Caulfields bade their neighbors and landlord goodbye and were driven to Yokohama by friends. Other friends were waiting at the pier to see them off. Even the young policemen whom Genevieve had tutored over so many years were there. When the farewells were all spoken and the little family had boarded the ship and descended to their cabin, they found a parting gift left by the policemen. It was a beautiful doll in a glass case.

A feeling of grief came over Genevieve. She wondered what would become of those fine young men in a Japan turned suddenly militant. And a shudder like a breath of cold air went through her. What would become of the fine young men all over the world unless people everywhere tried to understand one another and to live in harmony together, she asked herself.

Genevieve had been away from America a long while. Her nieces, who had been little girls when she left, were now vivacious young teenagers. Uncle Leonard had died, and Aunt Ducky was very ill. Genevieve was glad to be able to see her again before she too passed away the following December.

Americans, Genevieve found, were very interested in learning about Japan. She had no trouble getting lecture engagements. Mother Mary Joseph of the Maryknoll Sisters helped her arrange a tour. Genevieve had been a close friend of Mother Mary before she became a nun and that warm friendship had continued through the years. To Genevieve, the Mother House of the Maryknoll Sisters in Ossining was a second home.

Haruko loved America. She went everywhere with

her mother. They even paid a visit to the White House and met Mrs. Eleanor Roosevelt whose husband, Franklin Delano Roosevelt, had become President.

And now the time had come for Haruko to make her decision—whether to return to Japan where a good career was awaiting her, or to go with her mother to the uncertainties of Southeast Asia. But Haruko didn't see that she had any choice at all.

"Mama, my place is with you," she said earnestly.

"You must think carefully about it, dear, before you make up your mind," Genevieve warned her. "Remember I got along very well before I knew you so I don't need a crutch to lean on. I love you, Haruko, and I want you to be truly happy. You can't be unless you're doing what you really want to do."

"But, Mama, I really do want to help you," Haruko insisted.

"Well," Genevieve compromised, "why don't you try working for a while with the blind. Then if you still like it enough to go along, I'll take you."

So Haruko went to Overbrook for special training. The teachers soon discovered that she had a unique talent for inspiring her pupils and bringing out the best in them. Genevieve knew then that Haruko had a real vocation among the blind.

"Now I can take you with a free conscience," she told her daughter. And she laughed. "I am so happy,

93

dear. I would have missed you terribly, but I did not want you to come just because you thought it was your duty."

It was time to make plans for the voyage. Genevieve decided that they would go to Asia by way of Europe so that they could do some sight-seeing in London, Paris, and Rome along the way. It would be a pleasant vacation for them both. They booked passage on the *Britannic* for the third of September.

Meanwhile they worked harder than ever at all that had to be done before they left. They both attended classes at the Lighthouse Institute for the Blind in New York. And Haruko took an additional course in Girl Scout leadership.

That summer their spirits were cheered by a letter from Luang Pradit promising Genevieve that even if the government was not interested in her school he would do all he could to help her. Other more tangible help came from her old school, the Perkins Institution. It was a contribution of Braille slates, Braille writing paper, elementary schoolbooks, and two complete sets of embossed maps. The most important treasure of all was the metal plates upon which Perkins had embossed in Braille the Thai alphabet which Genevieve had compiled in Tokyo. Not to be outdone in generosity, the Mitsui Steamship Co. of Japan offered to ship all the heavy school materials to Bangkok free of charge.

But not everyone showed such approval of Gene-

vieve's project. Many of her friends were horrified at
the idea. They could not in the least understand why
Genevieve should be so determined to go to far-off
Bangkok when there was plenty of worthwhile work
right around home to be done.

"Why, it's foolish," they said. "Japan is fighting in
China, and war is ready to break out in Europe. The
whole world is in chaos. And the people you want to
help aren't even interested."

But Genevieve could not be dissuaded. On the afternoon of September 3, she and Haruko were given a last
Godspeed by the Maryknoll Mother House. It was the
simple ceremony that was held for all Sisters about to
leave for mission lands.

> "How lovely are the feet of them
> That bring the gospel of peace . . ."

The sweet voices of the nuns faded away on the last
words of the Departure Hymn. As the travelers went
to take their leave, Mother Mary Joseph put into
Haruko's hand the small mission crucifix which is pre-
sented to every Sister before she makes her journey.

Haruko's face lighted up as she took the cross.

"Thank you, Mother," she whispered. "I'll try to be
worthy of it."

Genevieve's family and her close friends came down
to the ship to see her off. As the *Britannic* slipped away
from shore, Genevieve's thoughts remained with her
mother. She had wanted so much to come along. But

Genevieve had not thought it right to fill Mama's last years with trouble and danger. She would have a comfortable home with brother Henry and his family. Just the same it had been hard to part from her. Genevieve was never to be with her again.

While the ship was crossing the Atlantic to London, Genevieve had plenty of leisure to think of what lay ahead of her in Thailand. She knew her friends had had good reason when they had tried to persuade her to stay home. She was going to Bangkok under very shaky conditions. The eight hundred dollars she was carrying in traveler's checks was all the capital she had been able to scrape together both to start her school and to live on until she could establish herself. It was far less than she had hoped for.

Her apprehension deepened when she reached England. Prime Minister Neville Chamberlain was at the time negotiating with Adolf Hitler to bring "peace in our time" with the surrender of Czechoslovakia. Munich, the city where that treaty was signed, was to go down in history as a symbol of appeasement and betrayal.

War fever gripped both England and the continent. In London and Paris it spread its miasma of fear. In Rome it shouted with the arrogant and blustering voice of Benito Mussolini, who had allied himself with Hitler. Everywhere the good and simple rhythms of homely

living were being drowned by the ominous clamor of
war.

Genevieve was thankful, then, for the haven of the
Maryknoll House in Rome where arrangements had
been made for her and Haruko to stay while they were
in the city. Here they were separated from the world's
chaos by peaceful walls. The quiet serenity reminded
her poignantly of the three-day retreat she had spent in
a Dominican convent before her First Communion.

From the Maryknoll House, Genevieve and Haruko
sallied forth the day after their arrival on an exciting
adventure. It was an audience with Pope Pius XI at
Castel Gandolfo, his summer palace. It had been arranged for her as a surprise by Monsignor Joseph Hurley, who was then in the Vatican State Department.
Genevieve had met him in Tokyo when he had been
secretary to Archbishop Edward Mooney, and they
had been good friends ever since.

On the last day of their stay in Rome, Monsignor
Hurley took Genevieve and Haruko through the crypt
beneath St. Peter's basilica to the small chapel that stands
before the wall behind which the great fisherman is
buried.

It was very quiet there, far removed from the turmoil
of the outside world. Before the simple altar Monsignor
Hurley said Mass for the blind children of Thailand and
the success of Genevieve's work among them. As her

Msgr. Hurley took them through the crypt in St. Peter's.

friend's voice rose and fell lovingly over the ancient ritual, Genevieve's mind reached out for strength to the humble fisherman who lay so near.

Suddenly up came her head in that old familiar child-hood gesture. She had been worried before about what lay ahead and had wondered more than once whether she should have taken the advice of those who had urged her to stay at home. But now she knew she had done what was right.

"Dear God," she prayed, "as once You helped Peter to feed your lambs, help me to bring light and life to the children of Thailand who are prisoned in darkness now. I want so much to be of use to You."

CHAPTER 7

THE SCHOLARS

Genevieve was dazed as she stepped out into the tropical sunshine of that blistering Bangkok afternoon. She
had just come from an interview with Luang Pradit.
She had gone so confidently to see him, buoyed up by
the enthusiastic letter he had sent her while she was in
the United States. But the man she met was obviously
far different from the one who had written the letter.

The interview had begun reasonably enough with

Luang Pradit explaining the requirements for starting her school. Donations could not be solicited, he told her, unless she established a Foundation. The Foundation Board would have to be made up of respectable citizens, each one of whom would have to be approved by the government.

This law had seemed fair enough to Genevieve who could see no difficulty at all in getting a board together if Luang Pradit helped her. But when she asked him to serve as chairman he quickly refused. He even excused himself from introducing her to influential people who might help her. Before the very short interview was over, he had made it quite plain that he was washing his hands of the whole affair.

Haruko was so angry her cheeks burned and her eyes flashed.

"Mama," she cried, "you were never treated like this in Japan. Let's go back there."

Genevieve smiled despite herself. She was remembering how long ago Mr. Yoshimoto had encouraged her, only in the end to dash all her hopes. But this hadn't kept her from going to Japan when her heart had called her there. Now she wasn't going to allow one man to turn her aside from her mission here in Bangkok.

"If we go, Luang Pradit won't be the one to suffer," she reminded Haruko. "It will be the blind children of Thailand. So I'm staying. I'm starting the school. After all, that's why I came."

When her mother talked like that, Haruko thought, it was like a bugle announcing battle. There was nothing else you could do but get in there and fight by her side.

"I'm staying too, Mama," she said.

Young Dr. Fonthong looked from mother to daughter with admiring eyes. He wasn't a politician but he loved his people and he wanted to help them all he could. He liked the spirit of these two women.

"I'm glad," he said. "I'll do everything I can. First I'll make a list of important people for you to see. Perhaps you can persuade some of them to join your board.

"Meanwhile you'll need a lot of publicity because teaching the blind is a new idea here. Nobody has even dreamed of it. I'll speak to some newspapermen about interviewing you, and I'll get you on radio too, and maybe some lectures can be arranged."

So Genevieve spent the next weeks on a round of interviews that took her all over Bangkok. She and Haruko came to know it well—a vibrant city of some three and a half million people sprawled along the Chao Phraya River and traversed by narrow streets and numerous canals. The banks of the canals were lined with houses. Some of them were fine-looking villas; others were of old, weathered teakwood standing above the water on strong piles. In the slum districts they were only one-room bamboo huts with roofs of corrugated iron. And they sagged over the narrow canals as though they were bowing to one another.

The canals themselves teamed with life. Children splashed and shouted everywhere among the thick water cress and the lotus plants with their red and white blooms. And there were always sampans. The country folk came down from the country in their little boats piled high with produce from their gardens. They did a brisk business with the housewives who, from overhanging balconies, bargained for each day's fresh vegetables. Vendors of goods, clothes, hot luncheons, and dime store novelties from the West poled about the canals, too, selling their wares.

But the vendors weren't confined to the canals. They seemed to be everywhere in Bangkok, spreading out their goods on the sidewalks in front of the dark little shops. There wasn't a square foot that wasn't in use. Bolts of gorgeous cloth, heaps of brilliantly-hued vegetables and fruits, lotus seeds, tamarind pods, bamboo sprouts, fresh ginger, turtle eggs, edible lizards, flattened dried frogs, small octopuses, live crabs—you could find almost anything in the Bangkok market places.

The Thais were a merry people. They swarmed through the streets, laughing and chattering and singing. Everywhere gay children darted in and out among the legs of the grownups, squealing with laughter. The Thai children were always happy. They were dearly loved by their parents.

As in so many countries of the Far East, the Thai were very conscious of family unity and responsibility. There was no need for the old, sick or disabled to seek

The canal teemed with life.

help outside the family circle. They also believed there was great merit in charity, and if the blind had no family to take care of their physical wants, they could always count on alms. The blind weren't suffering because everyone was quite willing to care for them. Then why was it necessary to go to all the trouble of teaching them to do things for themselves? Besides, it was obviously impossible.

This was the attitude Genevieve met everywhere she went. People listened with interest, but no one could be persuaded to be a board member of anything so fantastic as a school for the blind. Genevieve seemed to be getting nowhere.

Then one day she heard that the Princess Mother with her two young sons, King Ananda and his brother Phumiphon, had arrived in Bangkok from Switzerland for a short visit.

"Haruko, we are going to talk to the Princess Mother about our school," Genevieve said. "If she takes an interest in the blind, I'm sure the others will be more interested."

The Royal House of Thailand has always held a unique place in the hearts of the Thais. Legend says that their first king was a divinity who descended from Heaven on the back of a three-headed white elephant or, perhaps instead, a fabulous creature half-bird and half-man called a *garuda*. Because of this belief all subjects were once required on pain of death to prostrate themselves when in the presence of the king or any member of his house. The same penalty was inflicted on anyone who so much as touched royalty.

A wise king abrogated those laws at the turn of the century. And now the people no longer believe in the divinity of the Royal Family. But it is still deeply revered and its opinions highly honored. This was why Genevieve felt that the Princess Mother's approval of her project would give it great prestige.

"But do you think it's possible for us to meet so important a person?" Haruko asked. She was thinking of how difficult it would be to get into the Imperial Palace and see Emperor Hirohito.

"We'll do our best," Genevieve laughed. "I'll speak to Mr. and Mrs. Neville about it."

Genevieve felt sure that Mr. Edwin Neville, who was the American Minister to Thailand, would help her if he could. And she was right. One day shortly after she had talked to him, his wife phoned to say that they had an appointment with the Princess Mother. So Genevieve and Haruko and Mrs. Neville set out for the palace.

To Haruko's surprise, the Princess Mother was just as informal as any other person. She had trained as a nurse at Massachusetts General Hospital and, while in America, had become deeply interested in sociological work. She thought Genevieve's school for the blind was a wonderful idea.

Genevieve came away from that pleasant interview

with a lighter heart than she had had since her disillusioning talk with Luang Pradit. A few days later, another piece of good fortune came her way. A young, progressive army officer named Lieutenant Nonen came to see her. He had heard her speak and thought her school would be a fine thing for Thailand. He told her he had an idea that might help her.

"What you ought to do," he explained, "is put on an exhibition at our Constitution Fair which opens on the tenth of December. Let people see with their own eyes what you can do. Everyone will be there."

Yes, everyone who could make it would go to the fair. The Thais love fairs. The biggest of all is known as Constitution Fair, and it is held at Lumpini Park in Bangkok.

How gaily the grounds are dressed for the big event! Bright banners are strung up everywhere to furl and flap in the breeze. At night festoons of colored lights sparkle overhead. And, day and night, loud-speakers blare out a continuous stream of lively music. There are displays of goods and gadgets and the latest scientific achievements from nations all around the world.

Among these fascinating displays Genevieve set up her little booth. It contained just a table and a couple of chairs upon which she and her interpreter sat. The things on the table were commonplace indeed—some embossed maps, a typewriter, and a ball of yarn with knitting needles.

Strange, Genevieve thought as her hands moved with

a caress over the yarn and needles, how that lowly knitting skill I despised so as a child is here again to prove its
value to me.

Opening day of the fair dawned with a riot of life
and color as swarms of people converged on Lumpini
Park, tying up city traffic for miles. Laughing, chattering, playing and eating, they made their way over the
bright fair grounds.

With such interesting things to see everywhere who
will have time for me, Genevieve couldn't help wondering apprehensively.

But she need not have worried. Her simple little
booth quickly attracted its first crowd. She knit for
them. She typed for them. She traced continents and
capitals, boundaries and rivers on her embossed maps.
Patiently, through her interpreter, she answered the
questions that came hot and fast. By the time the crowd
was ready to move on even the doubters and the scoffers
were convinced she really could see with her fingers.

From then on Genevieve never wanted for crowds.
By the time the fair closed she had demonstrated to
countless visitors—old and young, rich and poor, government officials and even members of the Royal Family. Most important she had impressed a number of influential people. It was easier now to persuade them to
join her board. One by one, she was able to add new
members until shortly before Christmas she had enough.
She sent her list to the Minister of the Interior for
approval.

"What do we do now, Mama? Wait?" Haruko asked.

"Of course not, dear," Genevieve answered. "We can't waste time waiting. The next thing we do is to ask the mayor of Bangkok to provide us with a house for our school."

Though she should have been used to it by this time, Haruko never could believe her ears whenever her mother announced she was going to do some fearless thing like this. No matter how stubborn the mayor was, Haruko knew in the end he would have to give in. People usually did when her mother made up her mind she needed something and went after it.

So they went to see the mayor of Bangkok. Genevieve had to visit him twice and use a lot of persuasion. But finally he agreed to use municipal funds to pay the rent on a house they could use both as school and living quarters. They moved in the day after Christmas.

As soon as they had the house, Genevieve recruited some women volunteers to copy the Thai elementary readers into Braille.

"Now all we need are pupils," Genevieve told Haruko.

But where were they? A week went by and no one came, though everything was free and there had been plenty of publicity to make the fact known.

"Mama, how do we get our pupils?" Haruko asked.

"I've made up my mind—we're going to see the sister of the Little Princess," Genevieve answered promptly.

The real name of the Little Princess was Tahn Ying Lec, and she was a member of the Royal House of Thailand. Though she was now a grown woman, Genevieve was sure she would bring prestige and set a good example by attending the school. So off she and Haruko went to suggest their idea to the sister who took care of the Little Princess.

The sister thought it was all very foolish.

"Why, she's far too old. She's almost thirty," she remonstrated.

"I don't care if she's a hundred; we'll teach her if you'll just bring her in," Genevieve begged.

So on January 2, 1939, the School for the Blind in Bangkok finally opened its doors. The Little Princess was its only pupil, but she was a good one. She learned quickly and her eager pride was touching. Best of all she set a good example.

Soon the school had another pupil whose aunt, too, was a member of the Royal Family. The pupil's name was Sahataya and she was just seventeen. Her aunt, who was very fond of her, agreed to drive her to and from school every day.

By the time a third girl joined the school, the Little Princess, whose health was not good, had to stay home, so the school still had only two pupils. It began to look as though its enrollment would stick at that number.

"Mama, they still aren't coming. What do we do now?" Haruko asked.

"We'll visit their families and try to persuade them personally to bring their children to school," Genevieve answered. She was more determined than ever.

The first family they went to visit was that of a sixteen-year-old blind boy. His name was Trong Aht and he was the son of a provincial governor. He lived with his grandfather.

"If you will send Trong Aht to our school, we can help him," Genevieve promised the old man.

"It's impossible. There is no way to get him there," the grandfather replied shortly.

"He could come by pedicab," Genevieve suggested, because, after all, the grandfather was well-to-do and could easily afford the small expense. "It would only cost a few cents a day."

"Spend money on a blind boy?" the grandfather exclaimed as though Genevieve were asking for a fortune. "That's ridiculous."

Genevieve came away from the interview feeling very disturbed. She thought of the lonely boy she had left behind. She couldn't abandon him or all the other children whose parents thought a few cents a day or just a little trouble was too much to waste on them.

"Mama, if even the children's own families won't help them there's nothing we can do," Haruko was saying.

"Oh, yes, there is," Genevieve answered. "We can get a car and bring them in ourselves."

They bought a small second-hand car. It cost about three hundred dollars American money, but the owner said they could pay it in installments. Even then it took a big chunk out of the nest egg Genevieve had brought from America to live on until they were established. She didn't care. Someone had to think of the children and she was sure God had brought her here to do it.

With a car it was easy to enlist pupils. Haruko drove around every morning picking them up and every afternoon she returned them again to their homes. Their families thought it was all a lot of nonsense, but they didn't object because it wasn't costing anything and it was making their children happy.

In May all the members of Genevieve's board were given the official stamp of approval. Now she was free to accept donations. By this time she had six pupils, and a few people were beginning to wonder if there might be something to a school for the blind after all. A trickle of donations began to come in.

Then a new catastrophe struck. The mayor of Bangkok resigned and the new mayor refused to pay the rent.

"Mama, are we going to have to close the school after all?" Haruko asked anxiously.

"No," said Genevieve, "we'll get our board to put pressure on the mayor. Meanwhile we'll pay the rent ourselves."

So every month Genevieve paid out the rent money

from her fast dwindling nest egg. Nothing could stop her now. Six eager pupils depended on her.

No one before had ever told these children they could amount to anything. They couldn't believe their ears when this determined American teacher promised that if they applied themselves they could learn to live just about as normally as other people. But they were ready to try. They studied with a will and soon they were able to read the Thai Braille textbooks.

Then Genevieve took another step. Because her pupils would have no other reading matter than those books if all they knew was Thai, she began teaching them English. Up until this time only the privileged few in Bangkok had been taught a foreign language. And now here they were, blind children, being given that wonderful opportunity. They were so proud. They wanted to study all the time.

"Tomorrow will be a holiday," Genevieve told them one morning.

"Oh no! Oh no!" the chorus went up unhappily.

"What's the matter with you?" Genevieve asked in surprise. "Everyone likes a holiday."

"Not us!" the children cried. "We've already wasted so much time. We want to learn as much as we can."

When the people of Bangkok saw that the blind children actually were learning things, more and more pupils began to come to the school. Presently there were fourteen, far too many to be picked up in the little car. But by this time it was no longer necessary. The parents were glad now to cooperate by providing transportation.

Then one day Princess Bichitr, a prominent member of Genevieve's board, came calling. She too was impressed by the children's progress. She decided that something had to be done to arouse even more interest in the school.

Princess Bichitr was the head of a very progressive girls' school which was going to hold a three-day festival before it closed down for the two-week August vacation. There would be a large crowd of visitors at the school during those days and many of them would be influential and wealthy.

"Will your pupils come and demonstrate what they have learned, and then I'll ask for donations for you," the Princess said.

So Genevieve's pupils went to Princess Bichitr's festival. They didn't know much really. They'd only been to school six months. They could speak some English and read simple books in both languages. But the guests, who just couldn't believe blind people could learn anything, thought the children's accomplishments almost miraculous.

Suddenly everyone was proud to have a school like this in the city. Everyone wanted to have a share in helping things along. The donations poured in. Soon there was enough money to take care of the whole first year including an additional teacher on salary. There was even some left over to make a fine start on the second year. Another piece of good news came from the mayor who had at last agreed to pay the rent.

Genevieve had succeeded at what she had come to Bangkok to do. Her little school was well launched, and not with foreign money but through the love and enthusiasm of the Thais themselves. Now, freed of monetary anxieties, she could devote all her time to loosening the fetters of blindness from the bright eager pupils in her charge. The joyous words of Isaiah came to her mind.

"The people that walked in darkness have seen a great light." She spoke them softly to herself.

CHAPTER 8

THE WONDERFUL GIFT

"What's happening? What's happening?" the children in the schoolroom jumped to their feet crying to one another.

There was a great commotion in the street outside coming closer and closer to the schoolhouse. All at once the babble burst through the front door.

Genevieve and Haruko hurried out to see what it was about. Several people had pushed into the hall. Most of them were just onlookers who had been attracted by a Chinese woman who was screaming loudly and gesticulating in all directions. The woman had a tiny child with her. It was hard to tell at first if it was a girl or a boy because the head was shaved and it was wearing the usual Chinese garb of black trousers and white top.

"But it's a blouse instead of a shirt, so it must be a little girl," Haruko decided.

Then she let out a gasp of pity because the little girl was suffering so from malnutrition that she didn't even look human. As so often happens when people are starving, her stomach was bloated, but her cheeks were sunken and her little face with its protruding mouth had the shape of a pig's.

The little girl said nothing. She didn't cry or smile or make a single move. She just stood there straight and still as a statue.

"She's blind," Haruko suddenly exclaimed.

Genevieve and Haruko hadn't learned enough Thai to decipher what the woman was saying. But at last a young German boy who had come along managed to quiet her.

"It's Dr. Jacobson's son," Haruko said.

Genevieve knew Dr. Jacobson well. He had left his country when Hitler came to power and had come to Bangkok to set up practice. But for those who could not pay he had established a free clinic, and he took care of all Genevieve's pupils without charge.

Now the Jacobson boy explained in English with a strong German accent that his father had asked him to guide the woman to the school because he didn't know what else to do. It was a sad story. The little girl's mother had also gone blind from malnutrition. Then she had died, leaving the child completely alone. The woman who had brought her here was just a neighbor.

There would be no problem at all, Genevieve thought, if only we had a dormitory.

Through the boy, she asked if the little girl had any relatives. At this the woman began to scream again, pointing out someone in the crowd. It was a very young woman with a sullen face.

"I am her sister," the young woman admitted reluctantly. "But I am married now and I must take care of my husband. I owe everything to him. And that certainly leaves me no time for that child."

Genevieve sighed. She had heard such excuses before. It was typically oriental for a wife, once she had married, to renounce all responsibility for members of her own family. But of course the little girl had to be cared for by someone. Through Dr. Jacobson's boy, Genevieve began to haggle with the blowzy neighbor woman and the slim, sullen sister while the child stood quietly listening, her face expressionless.

Finally Genevieve came to an agreement. Each morning Haruko would pick up the little girl and take her to school. They would give her a good lunch at noon, and then in the afternoon Haruko would bring her back. The neighbor and sister between them would see that the child was fed breakfast and dinner and had a place to sleep.

Grumbling, the two women consented. A little help was better than none they reasoned.

So the school had a new pupil.

So the school had a new pupil. The little girl was so tiny that the other children called her "Nit," which means "Little One" in Thai. Genevieve didn't like that word because in English, of course, it means louse, so she changed it to Nittie. But everyone thought she was saying "knitting" and that became the child's nickname.

Strange, Genevieve thought with amusement, how this knitting bit follows me around everywhere. I can't seem to get away from it.

Little Knitting proved to be as quiet at school as she had been that first day she was brought in. She never talked or laughed. She hardly had the energy for anything. She was so weak from malnutrition that she couldn't sit upright for any length of time. Often when she was at handiwork they would find her slumped over the table with her head resting on it, too heavy to lift.

Knitting had a fine talent. Small though she was, she knew how to sew very well, even though she was blind and could not see what she was doing. They learned that before her mother died little Knitting had helped her make Chinese trousers to sell.

A lump came into Genevieve's throat whenever she thought of that sick mother and her child squatted in the dark hole of their room, stitching, stitching from early morning until late at night to earn a few pennies for food, never getting enough, starving, going blind, dying. Haruko's heart ached, too, every day she went for the little girl. She had to make her way through the Chinese quarters of Bangkok, a maze of twisting alleyways, some so narrow that it was difficult even for two bicycles to pass each other. Into those corridors the sun could scarcely penetrate between the high godowns, and the smell of rotting fish and vegetables was at times overpowering. Almost a million Chinese lived packed together here. Haruko hated to return the child to this ugly, teeming place.

Knitting was conscientious. She tried to do well all that was expected of her. The only trouble was she was so weak. She continued to faint at her work a dozen times a day. And she didn't get any better with time. It was obvious she was being fed very little if anything at home. She wolfed down the noon meal. But, hungry as she was, she would never take anything that wasn't given her, not even something as small as a piece of fruit.

Why I was like that when I was a child, Haruko thought. She and I are alike. Mama gave me love and life. I want to help Knitting.

"Mama, we have to do something about her; we can't let her go on like this," Haruko said one day. "She'll die."

Genevieve smiled.

"We *are* going to do something for Knitting, Haruko," she said. "Our bedroom is big enough for three, don't you think?"

"Oh, Mama," Haruko cried, and she put her arms around Genevieve.

Then she set up a little cot by her own bed in the room she shared with her mother. And little Knitting came to live with them. Because she was so small and weak, the other pupils all made themselves responsible for her. At recess time they watched over her. How quiet she was among the gay and playful Thai children.

Then one day something happened. One of the children ran to tell Genevieve about it.

"Teacher, teacher," she cried, "Knitting just laughed. She laughed right out loud."

It was the first sound that anyone had heard Knitting make during all the time she had been at school. But now her silence was broken at last there was no holding her back. She talked a blue streak, chattering away half in Chinese, half in Thai. Sometimes she fought wildly with the other children. Sometimes she would throw a tantrum, flinging herself on the floor and screaming until she was breathless. In the only way she knew how, the way of the street children among whom she had lived all her life, Knitting was fighting hard to keep her place in the school. She was terrified of being shoved out from the warmth and comfort she had found there. Most of all she wanted to be near Haruko. She never wanted to be separated from her. She loved her fiercely.

Haruko knew and understood and lavished her affection on the little girl. Gradually Knitting came to realize that there were other rules in the world besides the rule of yell and claw and fight. She learned the rule of love. She began to scream less and to laugh more. She was a vibrant child, and now, almost greedily, she reached out to rejoin the world of the living.

Her sight was irrevocably lost, but Dr. Jacobson removed her disfigured eyes and replaced them with two artificial ones. Good food put meat on her bones and plumped out her cheeks. Her face looked like a little girl's, not an animal's, now. Her hair grew and Haruko plaited it in shiny braids.

Gone, too, were the sober black trousers and white blouse she had worn when she first came to the school —black and white, the drab colors of the Chinese in Bangkok. Haruko turned her talents as a designer into a labor of love. She cut and sewed dress after dress for little Knitting until soon she had a fine wardrobe.

In one of these pretty dresses little Knitting was baptized one day. She was given the lovely name of Aurora —Aurora Lee. She called Genevieve "Mama" and Haruko "Sister." She accompanied Haruko everywhere about the city.

"Who is the sweet little Chinese girl, Haruko?" people they met would ask.

"Why, she's part of our family," Haruko would answer proudly.

That summer of 1940 Genevieve and Haruko decided to go for a week's visit to Japan. Their excuse was to pick up materials for the school. But really they were homesick and eager to see old friends again. It had been a year and a half since they had been away.

It was an uneasy time for travel. Over most of Europe the black swastika now fluttered. England alone remained a lonely bastion of freedom. In the Far East the fighting between Japan and China, which the

Japanese were still calling the "China Incident," was continuing, with Japan now in full possession of the coastal regions.

Fresh from free and easy Bangkok, Genevieve and Haruko discovered with a shock that Japan was even more of a police state than ever. The whole economy was geared for war. All kinds of poor substitutes were being used for fuel and clothing and food so that the ships could concentrate on bringing in scrap iron, rubber and oil.

Old friends, they found, were the same. They would always be the same. But everywhere else there was suspicion and fear. Stronger than ever now, the dreaded Kem Petai was poking and prying, questioning, arresting and jailing. People were afraid to talk openly or even to think freely now. It was as though they were walking around mentally in rooms where the ceilings are too low.

"Mama, I can't stand it here any more," Haruko said. "Let's go back home."

"Yes, dear, let's go home," Genevieve agreed. "They're waiting for us."

She was thinking sadly that home was no longer Tokyo now, but Bangkok—Bangkok that seemed so far removed from war and its ugliness.

With the opening of the next school term, Genevieve began to add more members to her family. This was because people out in the country were starting to hear of her and were bringing in their blind children. Genevieve didn't have the heart to turn them away so she and Haruko just put up more cots.

By this time Genevieve had established herself as a private tutor and was easily able to support herself and Haruko and Aurora. Now she stretched her budget to include the other children. But, oh, how she yearned for a dormitory. She prayed for it every day.

Then one bright morning in October a handsome young Japanese came calling. His name was Nobutsugu Utagawa. And he had been sent by another Japanese, Mr. Goshima, who had just arrived from Tokyo.

"Mr. Goshima is very interested in your school," explained the young man. "He wants to meet you and talk about doing something to help."

Help, thought Genevieve. The dormitory!

She couldn't wait until Mr. Goshima arrived.

"I have five children I'm boarding myself now," she told him when he came. "I can't take in any more, and I can't bear to send them away. A dormitory school would solve everything."

Mr. Goshima shook his head sadly. The dormitory dream was too big for him too, just yet, he told her. He had had in mind something more modest—say a hundred *baht* a month to help with the children's board. He didn't tell Genevieve that the hundred *baht* wasn't coming from a mythical anonymous donor, but out of his own monthly salary. He just began to pay it regularly.

Regularly too, Mr. Utagawa visited at the Caulfield home. Only they didn't call him Mr. Utagawa any more, but simply Nobu.

The more Genevieve saw of Nobu the more she liked him. He came of Christian parents and had high ideals and a great integrity. His family had not been wealthy enough to send him to school, but he had made his own way right up through the university. He was working for a Japanese business firm in Bangkok.

As the year lengthened to its close, Genevieve, who never missed much of what was going on around her, was beginning to be sure of one thing.

"My little daughter and Nobu are in love," she told herself happily.

And that was how Christmas came—the most joyful Christmas Genevieve was ever to know. It even included a Christmas tree that filled the house with a fresh, piny odor. Nobu had had it brought down from the mountains of northern Thailand as a surprise.

Christmas Day began with midnight Mass. Genevieve, Haruko, Aurora Lee, and Nobu attended it together. The day was to end with a party for the young people, but first there were gifts to be opened.

Genevieve's best gift that year didn't come under the Christmas tree, however. She received it through Mr. Goshima. He hadn't been content to let matters rest with the hundred *baht* a month he was already contributing. He had gone around collecting money from all his Japanese business acquaintances in Bangkok until he had four thousand *baht*. It was sufficient to get her longed-for dormitory school off to a good start.

"Why has Mr. Goshima shown so much interest in our school?" Genevieve asked Nobu, after she had recovered from her surprise at the generous gift.

"Just before he came here, Mr. Goshima met a paroled prisoner whom you once visited in prison," Nobu explained. "The prisoner talked so much about how you had comforted and encouraged him that when Mr. Goshima discovered you had started a school for the blind he couldn't rest until he had helped you."

Nineteen forty-one—so many things were afoot that year. Late in January, Haruko and Nobu told Genevieve what she had been expecting to hear since Christmas. They loved each other and wanted to get married.

Genevieve held both their hands in hers.

"I'm so happy," she told them. "Of course, it must be a big church wedding."

Bishop Peros granted the dispensation and the wedding was held in the Chapel of Mater Dei shortly after Easter. It was tropical April weather. The heavy fragrance of frangipani and jasmine filled the windless air. Flame trees flung flamboyant scarves of blossom against the sky. Every canal was a ribbon of white and scarlet lotus blooms.

The little chapel was crowded. Everyone who knew Haruko and Genevieve and Nobu had come to the wedding. Haruko and Nobu were at the altar now.

Genevieve was so happy that she felt like crying.

With the wedding over, it was time to concentrate on the new dormitory school. The first thing Genevieve did was to locate a much larger house with plenty of playground around it. But the old house that held so many happy memories wasn't to be deserted either. Haruko and Nobu wanted to keep it for themselves and they insisted that Genevieve continue living with them.

"After all, what would life be like without you around, Mama," Haruko wanted to know.

Once she had the dormitory school, Genevieve engaged Miss Vedhi as living-in supervisor. Then she hired two more Thai teachers. With the help of Haruko and Khun Ying Roseline, her faithful Thai volunteer, she was sure they could easily handle the additional pupils who would be coming in. But now it seemed to Genevieve that some of those pupils should come from out of town so that the country Thais wouldn't get the idea the school was just a city institution.

"Let's go to Chiengmai and enroll some blind children from up there," she said to her assistant, Miss Vedhi.

So Miss Vedhi bought the train tickets, and one day she and Genevieve were on their way to Chiengmai, which lies in the north of the little country in a high valley plateau among mountains clothed in teakwood forest and jungle. The way there led through the rich rice basin of Central Thailand watered by the Chao Phraya and its tributaries and crisscrossed by numerous canals. After the rains the whole plain would become a shimmering shallow lake in which the farmers would be busy setting out their tiny rice plants. But now, toward the close of the dry season, it stretched away, brown and barren, to the far horizon.

It was an overnight journey and by the time dawn came they had entered a different country of mountains and valleys, and the air was cooler. Now they were climbing steeply, the tracks running through thick jungle that glistened in the sunlight. Then they crossed a deep gorge on an airy trestle and presently came out on a high plateau, checkered with dry upland rice fields and watered by the bright coils of the winding river.

The train chugged across the plateau to Chiengmai, a dreamy little town that lay in the shadow of the great blue mountain of Doi Suthep. They had reached the end of the line. It was time to disembark. But they were not coming as absolute strangers. They had been invited to stay in the home of Dr. Court, an American missionary who was in Chiengmai to run the McCormick Hospital, a cooperative venture between Thailand and America.

Dr. Court not only served the people who lived in the open plateau, but the strange hill folk also whose ramshackle villages stood in clearings in the lush jungle and were reached at times by almost impassable paths. There was no illness or accident that he had not seen and cared for. Some he could cure, others he could only alleviate. But he was always there to help when he was called upon. And everyone but the jealous witch doctors idolized him.

Genevieve and Miss Vedhi saw little of the doctor during their stay at Chiengmai. But his influence was around to help them all the same. And by the time they were ready to leave they had enrolled six children in their school and made arrangements for them to follow by train in a couple of weeks. Then it was back again across the plateau toward the misty hills through which the train tracks dropped to steamy Bangkok. With luck they would get there before the rains began.

CHAPTER **9**

THE VALLEY OF THE SHADOW

Through 1941 Genevieve anxiously followed the progress of the war as it pushed closer and closer to Thailand. Since France had fallen to Germany, Japan was free to nibble away at French Indo-China and finally to occupy it. Japanese troops were now lined up along the Indo-China border of Thailand. Along the Malayan border British troops were pitched. Unhappy Thailand lay sandwiched between the two powers.

The only thing Prime Minister Phibul Songgram could do for his small nation was to issue a proclamation announcing that his country would fight on all borders against any invader. Bangkok went on about its business as usual, but an air of apprehension hung over everything. And from the outside world the ominous news continued to come in.

Germany was invading Russia. Bombers were still flying over England, and the war was flaming across North African deserts. Relations between America and Japan had reached the breaking point. Talk of war between the two nations was growing ever more persistent.

How far away the United States seemed to Genevieve then, how welcome a haven. It would be nice to be home safe again with Mama and Henry and Beatrice and the girls. But when late that fall an official from the American Embassy phoned to offer her passage either to Manila or America she didn't hesitate.

"Thanks all the same," she said, "but I can't leave."

She had twenty blind children for whom she felt as responsible as any mother, and an adopted daughter who needed her now more than ever before. At her doctor's orders, Haruko had quit teaching. X-rays showed she was going to have twins, and the doctor said they would probably be born prematurely—perhaps by as much as a month. But he didn't foresee any trouble.

When the little family thought of the new life that

was so soon to brighten the old house, war and its ugliness and dangers seemed a far way off. But of course this was only fancy. One day the explosion came, sooner than anyone expected, on a date that would go down in history—December 7, 1941. Even while Ambassador Nomura for Japan and Secretary of State Cordell Hull for America were working feverishly in Washington, D.C., to keep the peace, the military clique in Japan, acting on its own, attacked Pearl Harbor without warning.

Genevieve heard the news in the early morning of Monday, December 8. Because of the difference in time between Thailand and Hawaii, the attack had taken place during the night while she was peacefully sleeping. She listened in horror as the descriptions came crackling out—Pearl Harbor in shambles; ships and planes of the Pacific Fleet anchored there sunk or destroyed; planes strafing soldiers, sailors and civilians alike.

The country of her birth and the country of her adoption were at war with each other. The people she had loved, good people among whom she had lived for so many years, among whom she could count so many warm friends—even those dearest to her, Haruko and Nobu—had been transformed by this single act into her enemies.

While she listened, Genevieve was quickly dressing. There were important things to be taken care of. With the United States in the war Thailand couldn't hope to remain out of it much longer. And if the Japanese took over the little country it would doubtless be internment for her. She had to make arrangements for her children while there was still time.

She hurried out of her room. Nobu had to be told first.

"Japan attacked Pearl Harbor last night," she said to him. "It just came over the radio."

"Oh, Mother!" Nobu's voice was tense and shocked.

"I've got to go to the school at once," Genevieve went on. "I'll be back at noon."

She left it up to Nobu to break the news to Haruko, and, hurrying out of the house, hailed a pedicab and climbed in and was quickly on her way. It seemed to her as though part of her were doing all these things with the efficiency she had learned from long years of training while another part of her sat apart and grieved. Why? Why? Why? There was so much of want and pain in the world, why did not men everywhere band together to fight these foes of humanity instead of destroying one another.

But as soon as she arrived at the school she was all business again. Things had to be done. There was no time now for grief.

"Japan and the United States are at war," she told the horrified Miss Vedhi. "It will probably come to Bangkok soon. We must have a good supply of food for the

"Japan and the United States are at war."

children in case of shortages. Get all you can lay your hands on. Also better look into providing some kind of air raid shelter here—you never know. Meanwhile we'll run the school as usual."

At noon Genevieve returned home to find Nobu already there. His voice was grim as he gave her the news. There had been skirmishes on the border between the Japanese and Thais. But the Thais didn't have a chance. Japan had invaded. A large number of ships carrying Japanese troops had anchored in the mouth of the Chao Phraya River the previous night. And this morning the soldiers had disembarked and taken possession of Bangkok, too.

The war had come to Thailand. There was nothing Phibul Songgram could do but sign an agreement with the Japanese that would at least give his little country the status of ally and prevent her from suffering the fate of a vanquished nation. But the signing of that agreement made Genevieve an enemy alien, even in Thailand.

What would the future bring her? Would they put her in an internment camp along with all the other American nationals? She didn't know. But one thing she was sure of. If she closed the school now, she would probably never get it on its feet again. She was determined to keep it open as long as possible.

Just as she had expected, Genevieve soon lost her liberty. On the sixteenth of December she was placed under house arrest. A pleasant young policeman was stationed at her gates to enforce the order. But at least she was still free to conduct the business of the school by telephone. She realized how fortunate she was when two days before Christmas all the American, British and Dutch nationals, except those who served as government advisors, were rounded up and sent away to internment camps.

"Well, at last I suppose I have something to be grateful to Luang Pradit for," Genevieve said to Haruko with a laugh. "After all he did invite me here, even if he gave me no help once I came. So I guess that makes me a kind of official advisor too."

Haruko laughed with her. Those were the days they tried hard to find something to laugh over, because really there wasn't much humor in the world around them. The news that kept coming in over Genevieve's radio was growing grimmer by the day. Wake, Guam, the British-held Gilberts had all fallen quickly. An invasion of the Philippines was mounted. Christmas dawned, a cheerless holiday. Genevieve was not even allowed to attend the joyful Christmas Mass. While Nobu and Haruko went to church she sat alone in the quiet house listening to her radio pass along to her the dreary news of Hong Kong's surrender.

Three days after Christmas, on a Sunday, Haruko said, "Mama, it's time. I must go to the hospital now. Nobu will take me."

"I'm going too," Genevieve said. "I'm going with my daughter. Let's see them try to stop me."

She put on her hat and her coat and out of the front door she went. The guard was standing there, but he never said a word or made a move as Nobu helped first Haruko and then Genevieve into the car. Then they were driving away very fast.

"What happened to the guard?" Genevieve asked curiously.

"He was looking the other way," Nobu answered. "He was looking the other way most of the time."

When they got to the hospital, the Sister in charge gave Genevieve a room next to Haruko's. And she settled down there to stay until the babies came.

It was a long wait, because it wasn't easy for Haruko. Finally Monday evening the doctors decided on a Caesarean operation. And at six o'clock the babies arrived— a boy and a girl. They were normal healthy babies, but so tiny, because they were premature, that there was plenty of room for both of them in one crib.

What more could one ask of life, Nobu thought, looking proudly down at his children. In that moment it was almost easy to forget the ugly war.

Haruko, who was still unconscious, didn't see her babies until the following morning. She smiled happily when the nurses showed them to her. But she was weak and in pain. An infection had set in. Nothing the doctors tried could save her life. Her strength ebbed away fast.

On the third day, Haruko was given the Last Sacrament. Genevieve and Nobu were at her side when she died. Nobu was holding her hand. He had to bend over to hear her last words. They were ones of trust and faith.

"I have everything to live for," Haruko whispered. "But if God wants me now, I'm ready."

Then she was gone.

There is a grief that passes all other griefs; there is a desolation that knows no limits. And in those first moments in that still hospital room Genevieve entered that terrible place whose name is despair.

Where could she turn now for help—to God only, to God who had given her the gift of this young and vital girl and now had taken her away. So many times in the past Genevieve had simply not accepted the verdict, "Will of God." She had fought through obstacles and gained a victory and discovered that the real Will of God was to do battle to bring His Will about.

Now as she stood by Haruko's bedside she had to realize that she had come to a place where nothing could be won through battle, where she had to learn instead the difficult lesson of acceptance. This was truly God's Will.

"But why? But why?" her heart kept crying out.

Then suddenly as if a hand touched her shoulder and a voice spoke to her she thought of Nobu desolate and of Haruko's babies, motherless in a world of war. And she knew she could not indulge in the luxury of grief.

Haruko had left behind unfinished work, had left it trustingly, knowing that her mother would never fail her.

"And I won't," Genevieve said to herself.

Up came her chin again. Her shoulders straightened in that familiar way.

"Give me the strength to do the things that have to be done," she prayed.

First there was the funeral. It was held at Assumption Cathedral. Only after it was over did Genevieve return to the big empty house where the guard still stood and still politely looked the other way. But Genevieve couldn't stay in the house while the twins were separated from her. The Sisters had agreed to care for them at the hospital until they were three weeks old, so every day she went there with Nobu to visit them.

Genevieve felt very sorry for Nobu. During those first days he was so bewildered by the sudden tragedy that he was like someone walking in his sleep. But all the while one thing kept coming back to him—the memory of Haruko's dying words and the calm surrender in her face as she had slipped away from him.

"I want to study the Catholic religion," he said to Genevieve one day. "It meant so much to Haruko."

Genevieve smiled.

"Haruko will be pleased," she said, for she knew that though Haruko was gone she still prayed for her family's welfare. That was the meaning of the Communion of Saints.

When the twins were just a week old, Genevieve and Nobu took them to the Chapel of Mater Dei for their christening. It was a grand affair with Bishop Peros there to officiate. The twins were given both Japanese and Western names. The boy was called Nobuyuki Joseph Samuel, and the girl, Haruko Marie Thérèse. After the christening, Genevieve and Nobu returned the twins to the hospital. In two more weeks they would be home for good.

That very day Bangkok had its first taste of war. Enemy planes flew overhead and a few bombs fell. Panic seized the city. Even the polite policeman who guarded Genevieve's house was affected. He remembered there was a war on and his prisoner was an enemy alien. The next day he asked Genevieve not to go out any more.

"All right, I'll stay in," she promised, grateful that he had permitted her to accompany Haruko and be with her at the end.

But now that she could no longer leave the house, its loneliness became almost unbearable. It seemed so empty just because it had been so full before of Haruko. Everywhere she turned, she seemed to come across reminders of her daughter. It was good, then, to be able to busy herself with preparations for the twins.

First the nursery had to be got ready, with twin bassinets, bottles and sterilizer and baby bath. Next came the problem of milk.

There was no such thing as falling back on cow's

milk though there were plenty of cows in Bangkok. They were almost exclusively in the hands of the Indians who always watered their milk. It was so common a practice that no one even dreamed of asking an Indian if the milk he was selling was watered, only by how much. The water came from the canals and helped to spread diseases like cholera and typhoid. The twins would have to have tinned or powdered milk. Genevieve began phoning her friends and asking them to look for it for her.

They did. They scoured all the markets in the city. And though imports were now cut off and foreign supplies were fast dwindling they turned up can after can. At last Genevieve had fifteen cases, enough to last a year.

Getting a nurse to help with the twins was as important as finding enough milk, but much more difficult. At last, though, even here Genevieve was successful and the babies came home to stay.

And now a strange thing happened. Suddenly the old house that had seemed so dead and empty before became alive again. It was as though the babies had brought life and healing with them. And how could it be otherwise, for they were Haruko's children and with them nearby it never could seem as though Haruko herself were very far away.

CHAPTER **10**

WAR COMES TO BANGKOK

"Goodbye, Mother. Take care of yourself and the twins while I'm gone," Nobu said anxiously.

It was early in February and he was leaving Bangkok because his government had ordered him to Burma to act as liaison man between the Burmese Independence Army and the Japanese government. Nobu was so idealistic he firmly believed his country meant to give Burma complete freedom once she had won independence from Britain. And he wanted to help the project along.

It was useless for Genevieve to try to convince him the Japanese militarists would never keep their word. Sooner or later, she knew, he would find out the truth for himself and she felt sorry for him when that time came. She was also worried for his safety in Burma, and for their own here in Bangkok.

Over her short-wave radio, which the Thai authorities had allowed her to keep, the grim news continued to come in. The Philippines, Burma, New Guinea, Malaya, Borneo, Sumatra, Java, all were falling to the Japanese. Thailand was lost too, because she had not only proclaimed herself an ally of Japan but had even issued a declaration of war against the Allies.

Of course many Thais didn't approve of this. The Thai Minister to the United States wouldn't even deliver the declaration of war because he said it had been made by the Thai government only under pressure. And soon a Free Thai underground began to work actively with the United States and Great Britain.

Despite its new close ties with Japan, the Thai government decided Genevieve wasn't such a dangerous enemy alien after all. One day she was told she might go anywhere she wished if she was accompanied by a guard. Her guard turned out to be a pleasant young Thai named Kun Sorn.

"Miss Caulfield, Miss Caulfield, welcome back again!" the children greeted her joyfully when she showed up that first day riding in an official pedicab tricycle driven by Kun Sorn. They had missed her and they wanted to show off what they had learned while she was away. It was a lesson of war—an air raid drill.

Miss Vedhi had provided the school with two very novel shelters. The city is built on earth so saturated with water that it is impossible to dig a hole of any depth without its becoming a pond, so Miss Vedhi had simply had two huge cement jars sunk into the ground. Each jar was capable of holding ten to twelve people, and notches had been chiseled down their interior sides to serve as steps. Now at Miss Vedhi's direction, the children demonstrated for Genevieve how quickly and efficiently they could leave the school and dash down those steps to the bottom of the jars.

"You should see the visitors stare," Miss Vedhi told Genevieve proudly. "They just can't believe blind children could be as nimble as this. They say it's as though they have eyes."

All over town the Thais were providing themselves with similar underground shelters or crude ones above ground. They would have been small protection in case of a near hit. But they looked strong and gave the Thais a feeling of security.

Genevieve and the twins had a place they could use too. The neighbors across the street had invited them to share the little cement shelter they had built in their garden.

Generally it was night when the air raid siren

sounded. Then there would be a great stir in the house and nurse, cook, babies and Genevieve carrying a basket filled with necessities would cross the street to the shelter. It was always full of people and one dog—the neighbor's pet which they could not bear to leave outside. It would cower in a corner of the small room, and every time a bomb exploded it would growl in a low, menacing tone.

Usually the babies slept quietly, one in the nurse's arms, the other in Genevieve's. Very little disturbed them. Now and then, however, one of them would cry out and have to be comforted or changed or fed. At last the sound of the droning planes would fade in the distance and the all clear would sound. Then the little procession would head back again for the house and the interrupted night's sleep.

But Genevieve had another danger besides the bombs to worry about. That was her status as an enemy alien in Thailand. So long as the lenient Thai government kept control of the situation she felt safe. However the Kem Petai were operating in Bangkok too. As yet they had power only over their own nationals, but they used it ruthlessly to imprison many fine Japanese men, including kindly Mr. Goshima who had raised the funds for Genevieve's dormitory school.

Genevieve couldn't help wondering what would happen to her if the Kem Petai, exasperated by the work of the Free Thai underground, should demand jurisdiction over Bangkok's enemy aliens also. Of course it might seem strange that anyone would suspect a blind woman of spying, but Genevieve kept remembering the arrogant voices of the Kem Petai men who had questioned her in Tokyo and a shiver would go through her.

One day while she was worrying about her situation she received a call from the Swiss consul.

"Our country is assisting with the repatriation of internees in Thailand," he told her. "If you wish we can arrange for you to return to the United States."

It was Genevieve's second chance to go home. And how tempting was that offer! The only trouble was she still couldn't turn her back on her twenty blind children, or Haruko's motherless babies.

"Thank you very much," she said firmly, "but I think I'll just stick it out. It's impossible for me to leave now."

April, the last of the dry months, arrived under the shadow of war that year. But to the farmers in the countryside war was practically non-existent. All their thoughts and prayers were for the coming rains. Until they fell, the rice fields in Thailand's great central plain could not be planted.

On April 13, which is the Buddhist New Year, Songkram, the Water Throwing Festival, was celebrated with a will. In all the Buddhist temples, prayers were offered for plentiful rains and fine crops and good fortune of every kind. People went round sprinkling one another with water—the more mischievous young folk splashed whole bowlfuls of it on any innocent passerby—accompanying the water with a blessing. Now the country stood poised for the monsoon season.

It came one afternoon with great black thunderclouds and the crackle and rattle of lightning and thunder, with the rush of a strong gale bearing on its back cascades of rain. The cloudburst lasted for half an hour. Then it was all over and the sun returned as hot as ever.

That first rain was followed by others like it. They became more and more frequent as the season progressed until presently every blistering day was marked by at least one heavy tropical outburst. By June the monsoon season was very well launched.

In June, Genevieve bade goodbye to all her American friends who were being repatriated. It gave her an empty feeling to see them go. Shortly afterwards Nobu returned for a visit.

"I'm so grateful to you, Mother, for staying to take care of the children," he said. His face filled with affection as he looked at the twins. They were fat and happy and healthy. A far cry he thought from the tiny babies he had left in February.

That year was a year of heavy rains, and by September the city of Bangkok was lying almost completely under water. Only those who lived in two-story houses were in luck. They just moved their belongings to the top story. Up went everything at the school and in Genevieve's home. Even her little car was lifted onto the high verandah.

Despite the floods, however, no one went hungry. Food still came in from the country in little sampans. And there were plenty of fish to be had simply by casting nets from second-story windows. People carried on business by boat now. And this was how Genevieve went to school.

Actually the floods were a blessing because with Bangkok under water the Allied planes couldn't locate any targets and didn't bother to come over at all. But of course this pleasant respite couldn't last forever. In the dry autumn weather that followed, the waters began to fall and by Thanksgiving the planes were back again. Genevieve and her school children together with all the rest of Bangkok had to settle down once more to nights of uncertainty and fear.

Nineteen forty-three brought new problems for Genevieve. The twins had been growing so fast their clothes had become too small for them. The embargo on imports had cleared the Bangkok stores of ready-made things and materials. But yarn was still available.

"The twins will have to settle for knitted clothes," Genevieve told herself.

With her needles clicking away once more, she added with a smile, "Well, isn't it funny! Here I am back at the knitting again!"

Despite the floods, however, no one went hungry.

Another problem was milk. The twins had run through all the cases Genevieve had accumulated and there was no more to be found in the stores. Cow's milk was still out of the question. One day Genevieve turned up an Armenian with a goat, and the twins had fresh goat's milk from then on.

The third problem was much more difficult. It was one of finances. Genevieve personally had no worries even though the study of English had fallen into such disfavor that all her pupils had dwindled away. Nobu saw to it that she had a big enough allowance to take care of the house and the twins and herself.

The school was a different matter. Once more it was

running out of funds. And no one seemed interested enough to do anything about it. The uncertainties of war had made people forget the needs of twenty blind children.

If someone doesn't help out soon, we'll have to close, Genevieve thought. I must find a way.

She prayed for guidance and help. And that was how her birthday came around.

"Happy birthday! Happy birthday!" the children chorused as she arrived at school that May 8. They had a birthday surprise waiting for her. She was shown into the auditorium along with the other teachers. Sahataya came out on the platform.

"We are going to put on two plays in honor of your birthday, Miss Caulfield," she explained. "The first play will be 'Cinderella' and it will be in English."

"My goodness!" Genevieve murmured. "In English!"

The curtain was raised and the play began. In the opening scene Cinderella crouched in the ashes of the fireplace while her cruel stepmother scolded her and her half sisters sneered. The play went on from there. Genevieve listened proudly. The children were word perfect, but that wasn't all. They were acting with genuine feeling. In fact, each and everyone of them was a kind of Cinderella—Cinderella sitting in the corner in the dark until Genevieve, their fairy godmother, had come along and waved her wand and showed them a magic new world. No wonder they were able to put so much expression into their performance.

"Cinderella" came to an end and was followed by a play in the Thai language which Sahataya herself had written. It turned out to be remarkably good.

If people could just see this beautiful show, I'm sure we'd get enough money to keep us going, Genevieve was thinking. I wonder if . . . Yes, we'll have to! She had made up her mind. She would find someone to help her stage a program to raise some money.

But before Genevieve could get round to doing this, the phone rang. It was Madame Phibul Songgram's secretary. Madame Songgram, the wife of the prime minister, was also president of the Women's Culture Association and her secretary was phoning to ask Gene-vieve's children to entertain the group.

The Women's Culture Association! You couldn't ask for a better audience anywhere because there are no more enthusiastic patrons of sociological projects than Thai women. If they once got interested in the school, anything could happen.

"But do you think they can do it?" the secretary was saying a little dubiously.

"Of course they can do it," Genevieve answered the secretary promptly.

As soon as she hung up, she sent for Sahataya.

"Sahataya," she said when the girl stood before her, "the Women's Culture Association has asked us to entertain them. Do you think you can put on those two plays you did for my birthday? It will mean the world to us."

"Don't worry, we'll do it, Miss Caulfield," Sahataya promised and her voice glowed.

Off she went to gather the children together.

"Miss Caulfield has worked hard to get our school started," she told them. "But it's our school really and now it's up to us to keep it going. So let's get to work."

"Yes, let's," the children agreed.

From then on, every spare moment they had went into rehearsals. Not one of them begrudged the time. After all it *was* their school.

153

"We're ready, Miss Caulfield," Sahataya said confidently when the great day arrived.

Genevieve thought it would be nice to have such self-assurance. But she knew how treacherous stage fright is. You can be very confident until the moment you step on stage. Then everything deserts you. It happens to the best of actors. And her children were only amateurs with the most important women in Bangkok as their audience.

The curtain went up. The show began. Genevieve held her breath at first. Then she let it out slowly. She didn't know whether any of the children were afraid inside or not. From first to last not one of them showed it. All around her she heard whispered ejaculations.

"Amazing! Impossible!"

"Those children are *blind?*"

Genevieve's pupils were putting on a performance so flawless it would have been a credit anywhere. Love for their school and pride in themselves were seeing them through.

When the program was over and the last applause had died away, Madame Songgram rose to her feet.

"Thank you, children, for a wonderful entertainment," she said.

Then she concluded with the promise Genevieve and the children had been waiting anxiously to hear. They were to receive a generous donation. The school had funds again.

It's always this way, Genevieve reflected. After you've done everything possible yourself, you can rely on God to take care of the rest of it for you.

Madame Songgram's donation wasn't all. A short while later, the Prime Minister himself sent over another as generous, accompanied by an invitation to teachers and pupils to join him and his wife for luncheon the next day.

And now it was Genevieve's turn to perform. She talked to the Prime Minister earnestly about what she had hoped to accomplish by coming to Thailand to start her school for the blind.

"I thought if people once realized how little it really takes to run a school of this kind it would open their eyes to the need of all people with handicaps—the crippled and the deaf, too," she explained. "Everyone should have a chance to lead a normal life."

The Prime Minister asked a few questions, but mostly he just listened.

"Well, I hope something comes of it," Genevieve thought as she and the other teachers and the children took their leave. She couldn't help worrying, however. Perhaps she had muffed her lines. The Prime Minister had said so little in reply to all her eloquence.

Within the next few days Genevieve learned just how convincing a performance she had put on. She was notified that the Department of Public Welfare of the Ministry of Health had decided to appropriate twenty thousand *baht* a year to the support of the Bangkok School for the Blind.

Twenty thousand *baht* a year in the middle of a war. It was almost unbelievable. It meant the school could grow, that more children could be equipped to do the work for which God had created them. Genevieve's heart was filled to overflowing.

It was only a short while later that Genevieve met Princess Visakar Svasti, great-granddaughter of famous King Mongkut, Rama IV. Princess Visakar, who was twenty-one years old, had just come from Malaya where she had been attending a convent school when the war broke out. After taking instruction for five years, she had become a Catholic against the objections of the Royal Family. Her Christian name was Mary.

Mary was weak and ill from malnutrition because in Malaya the Japanese occupation troops had confiscated all the food leaving the native population to starve.

"But when I'm strong enough, I want to come and help you," she told Genevieve.

So after a while Genevieve acquired a new volunteer teacher—one that added real prestige to the school, for Mary's great-grandfather had been Thailand's most revered king. The children loved her. But they weren't the only ones whose lives were enriched by her coming. This honest and selfless young girl answered a deep

156

need in Genevieve's life, lighted a place left dark and vacant with Haruko's going.

There was something about Genevieve, too, something noble and strong and warm, that drew Mary to her. It wasn't long before the girl was making long visits after school at Genevieve's home. And when she picked up the twins and hugged and kissed them it was as tenderly as ever Haruko could have done.

Just one shadow lay between Mary and the twins and that was the fact that their father was a Japanese. She couldn't forget how cruelly the population of Malaya had been treated by soldiers of his race.

If only Nobu would come back so Mary could get to know him, Genevieve thought. She would see that the real Japanese are not like this at all.

It wasn't long before Genevieve's wish came true. Nobu returned to Bangkok in mid-December. Like Mary he was thin and weak from malnutrition, and disillusioned besides. By this time he had come to realize with certainty that Japan had no intention of keeping her word with Burma. All the same, he had continued bravely working against the powerful Japanese military clique for the rights of the Burmese, until he was now too ill to work at all.

Nobu's loss of health was one more sign of the increasingly serious situation in which Japan was finding herself. Allied sea victories had mortally crippled her navy, and submarines were daily severing her supply lines. Unable to replenish their stores, the Japanese invaders were starving along with the civilian populations of the countries they had conquered and ravaged of food.

The growing strength of the Allies was apparent in the increased air raids over Bangkok itself. People were beginning to move to the country to escape them. Genevieve, too, had been looking around for a place to which she could evacuate the children in case of necessity. The Salesian Fathers at Bangtarn had offered her two small rooms in their crowded school. However, Genevieve didn't want to take advantage of their generosity unless it was absolutely necessary.

"After all," she told herself, "the planes are doing a good job of concentrating on military targets—the gasoline factory, the railway bridges, the shipping in the harbor. There's nothing really to be worried about."

CHAPTER **11**

OUR BROTHER'S KEEPER

It was the night of December 23, two days before the birthday of the Prince of Peace, and the air raid sirens were sounding again over Bangkok.

"Shall we leave for the shelter now, Miss Caulfield?" the nurse came in to ask.

Genevieve shook her head.

"I don't think it'll be necessary," she said. "Just let the twins sleep."

She turned to Nobu.

"They've been doing such precision bombing," she explained, "that frankly I've begun to feel safer here than in the shelter, because that dog goes crazy every time the bombs start exploding."

They blacked out their lights along with the rest of the city and stayed in the house. Presently the hum of sky-born engines came to their ears. The hum grew to a drone and the drone to a roar. Then the thunder of the first wave of planes was passing overhead. But these planes weren't going in search of military targets. They were unlike any other planes that had ever flown over Bangkok. Afterwards no nation would take responsibility for them or their terrible work of that night.

The first planes dropped flares lighting up the city like an illuminated map. With the flares to guide them the second wave of bombers unloaded their cargoes. Their target was the city itself. The dull thud of exploding bombs tortured the air. The earth began to shake as though in the grip of a giant quake.

Genevieve thought of the twenty children at the bottom of the jars in the school yard. They would have hurried there at the first air raid sirens. How fragile those jars seemed to her now. She spoke a prayer of thanksgiving when the first wave of planes passed on and the night was quiet again.

But the lull didn't last. Soon another wave was on its way. More bombs began to fall in an aimless pattern of destruction, and some of these were incendiaries. Blossoms of flame burst up here and there and crackled greedily among the wooden ramshackle houses of the poor. Flying sparks lighting on wooden roofs spread the blaze.

"Oh, Nobu, I'm so frightened for the children," Genevieve cried. "I wish we had them with us."

"Don't worry, I'll go after them," Nobu answered reassuringly.

During the next lull he slipped out of the house, but he hadn't even reached the garden before a third wave of bombers was overhead pinning him down.

Genevieve sat in the dark house with her hands clenched, thinking of the two small rooms at Bangtarn. They no longer seemed cramped and inconvenient to her.

Oh, why didn't I send the children there? she thought.

Then she realized how foolish it was to be blaming herself for the past. She was in the present. And in the present there was only one thing left to do.

"Keep them safe this night, dear God," Genevieve prayed. "And I'll send them to Bangtarn as soon as I possibly can."

Still the planes kept coming on, wave after wave. The city writhed under the merciless bombardment. Many people were trapped by falling debris or in burning homes. And the narrow streets were clogged by terrified fugitives.

At every lull Nobu kept trying to set out for the school. Each time he could get no farther than the garden before the bombs would be falling again. On his last attempt he came hurrying joyfully back.

"They're here, Mother. They're all here," he shouted.

Genevieve could hardly believe her ears. But there they were—Miss Vedhi and the children coming through the garden. They crowded into the house tired but jubilant. Outside the bombs were still falling. Those within scarcely heeded them now. They were all safe together. That was the only thing that mattered.

Miss Vedhi began to explain how when sparks had started flying everywhere she had decided the school should be abandoned. She had brought the children out of the jars and lined them up two by two and led them to Genevieve's house along Sathorn Road where there were no fires. Whenever a plane came over, she had made her charges lie flat on the ground so as not to attract attention.

In this way, starting and stopping at intervals, they had taken a long while. But one thing had guided them and given them courage all the way, so that even the youngest of them had not thought to complain. That was their trust in Genevieve. She would know what to do, they had told one another. No matter what, she would know—if they could just reach her.

Their faith touched Genevieve.

"Yes, I know all right," she agreed. "I should have done it before. I'm sending you off to Bangtarn."

At last the all clear sounded. Bangkok could draw in its breath, go to work on its fires, gather up its dead and injured, lick its wounds. In Genevieve's home, it was time for bed. The children stretched out on the floor wherever there was room and were soon peacefully asleep.

At last the all clear sounded.

It was Christmas Day when the pupils with Miss Vedhi set off for Bangtarn. Genevieve and the twins stayed behind with Nobu. Genevieve had work to do in town. She had to find new members to serve on her board in 1944. She had to make arrangements for the little group's support in Bangtarn.

163

"And, most important of all, I'll have to look around for a bigger place," she told herself. "Twenty children can't go on living indefinitely in those two small rooms without even electricity or running water."

But what of Mary? Her family, too, was planning to leave Bangkok and they wanted her to come along with them, so she was once more faced with a choice. And what a choice it was! On the one hand a fine, big house set in beautiful countryside, days of leisure, good food and pleasant pastimes. On the other, two cramped rooms which she would have to share with Miss Vedhi and twenty children.

Instead of leisure there would be work, very hard work. All the water would have to be drawn from the canals. The oil lamps would have to be cleaned and trimmed daily. The market place was so distant it could be reached only by slow, crowded trains. It didn't look like much of a choice for a princess used to luxury.

The interesting thing was that if it had all been up to Mary she wouldn't have hesitated a minute. Mary was the kind of girl who couldn't enjoy leisure and good food and fun while there was work to be done and people who needed her. The choice was only whether she wanted to serve badly enough to oppose her family's wishes again as she had when she decided to become a Catholic. The Royal House of Thailand is a very closely knit affair, and they weren't just asking Mary to go with them. They were insisting upon it.

All that Christmas, after the children and Miss Vedhi had gone, Mary wrestled with her problem. By night she had reached a decision. She came to see Genevieve about it.

"I've decided to go to Bangtarn," she said. "I can't run out on the children—or you either, Miss Caulfield."

Genevieve's face lighted up. She reached out and took the girl's hand.

"Oh, Mary, dear," she said, "I'm so glad and proud too."

That night Mary met Nobu for the first time. Almost from the beginning she began to see that Genevieve was right when she had said not all Japanese were like the Malayan occupation forces. Before the evening was over, she and Nobu had become good friends.

It was just before Easter of 1944 that Genevieve found the house she wanted for her children. It was a big brick one in Hua Hin, a delightful resort on the shores of the Gulf of Siam. The king's summer palace was right next door, yet the rent was modest. The children were moved there as quickly as possible. By summer Genevieve was able to join them. Nobody tried to stop her. There were far more important things to worry about.

The Axis was falling apart. On June 4 Rome surrendered. On June 6 the Allies invaded France. By August 25 Paris had fallen and the Allies were racing on to Germany from every side. In the Pacific, America was about to throw her brand new B-29s into action. These great super-fortresses had a far wider range than any other planes of their day. Soon Japan could expect massive air raids over her home islands.

The end was as plain to Prime Minister Phibul Songgram as to anyone. He had bet on the wrong side even though he had really had no choice about it. There was nothing he could do now except resign, making way for a new prime minister.

The school was not affected by the change. It was an established institution in Thailand. No one thought of cancelling the subsidy of twenty thousand *baht* granted by Phibul Songgram's government.

At Hua Hin, Genevieve found the children having the time of their lives roaming the countryside, getting their feet wet in the slow sea surf, becoming acquainted with God's earth away from the city. The twins loved it, too. They were two and a half years old now and they scampered about everywhere, chattering away in English and Thai, with some Japanese thrown in. They were healthy and happy and easily satisfied.

May 7, 1945, was a red letter day in the history of the world, for on that day Germany surrendered unconditionally. On May 8 the war in Europe was over. Now everything was concentrated in the Pacific. Hard fighting recovered the Philippines for the Allies. Iwo Jima and Okinawa were stormed and taken. The big B-29s were pulverizing every city and town of any size in Japan. There was talk of an invasion.

Then, on August 6, word came over the radio of a strange and terrible new bomb which an American plane had dropped on the Japanese city of Hiroshima, practically obliterating it. Three days later, on August 9, Nagasaki, like Hiroshima, was wiped out by a similar bomb. On August 15 the Emperor's voice over the radio was heard for the first time in history by the Japanese people:

". . . It is according to the dictates of time and fate that we have resolved to pave the way for a grand peace for all the generations to come by enduring the unavoidable and suffering what is insufferable . . ." He was saying that the war was over and Japan had lost.

Peace had come at last to a war-battered world. Emergencies were over. Mary's conscience need no longer trouble her if she chose to return to her family and make her peace with them. But Mary was an unusual kind of princess. She had already made up her mind to stay permanently with Genevieve and help with the school and the twins.

Back in Bangkok, British troops were now patrolling the streets. British authorities helped Genevieve find another schoolhouse for her children. It was the British, too, who enabled Genevieve to solve the problem of the twins' milk for the last time.

One day she brought up the subject to a soldier who had stopped to visit her.

"Why, we have so much tinned milk, it's running out of our ears," the soldier laughed.

"I'd like to buy some from you then," Genevieve told him.

The soldier looked from her to the garden where a big white goose was strutting about. Since the war burglars had become so numerous and bold that the cook had brought the goose to act as a kind of watchdog. He was supposed to cackle if trespassers entered the garden. But the fussy, old fellow cackled all the time and had a nasty disposition besides. He hadn't a friend in the world until all of a sudden the Britisher was staring affectionately at him.

"Tell you what," he said to Genevieve, "we've had nothing but tinned rations all through the war and we're hungry for fresh meat. I'll gladly exchange our milk for your goose."

So the deal was made. The British soldier went off with the goose under his arm. And Genevieve had all the milk the twins would ever need.

Peace brought more than milk to Genevieve. One day she received her first letter from the United States in almost four years. It was from brother Henry and it was already a year old. Mama had died, he said, in 1942. The news made Genevieve glad all over again she hadn't brought Mama to Bangkok to spend her last years under the shadow of war. Just the same, her going left an emptiness.

Peace affected another member of Genevieve's little family in a different way. For Nobu it meant internment along with all the other Japanese in Thailand. They had to live together in a large camp outside of town until they could be repatriated.

It was at Eastertime of 1946, when Nobu was allowed to come home for a two week visit, that he told Genevieve something which she had been expecting to hear for some while. He had asked Mary to be his wife and she had accepted. Just as she had decided in favor of the two cramped rooms at Bangtarn, she was ready to endure the hardships she would find in Japan for the sake of the man she loved.

"I'm so happy for you and Nobu and the twins, Mary," Genevieve said joyfully as she kissed Mary.

The knowledge that they would one day all be together again made it easier for the little family to part when, in June, Nobu left Thailand aboard a Japanese ship which carried three thousand other men, women and children back to their homes. He had promised to send for his family as soon as he could guarantee their support. Meanwhile, since English had come back into favor, Genevieve and Mary could earn a comfortable living tutoring.

The school, too, was in fine circumstances. It had grown so that the twenty thousand *baht* subsidy was no longer sufficient to support it. But this didn't matter because it had caught the imagination of the city, and donations were coming in from everywhere. The school could stand alone at last.

It had been Genevieve's dream, when this day came, to be able to find a Thai national to run the school. But now she found that the Thais were afraid to accept the responsibility. So she appealed to the Salesian Sisters who had been in Thailand a long while and knew the ways and customs of its people.

"We'd like to help but it sounds so difficult," they told her doubtfully.

Genevieve's persuasiveness, however, conquered their fears, and so they sent her Sister Rose to be trained for the work. Sister Rose was wonderful. She seemed to have a special talent for teaching and her heart was in it too. She learned fast, which was a good thing, because in May of 1947 a letter arrived from Nobu sending for his family. He had started a little business bringing fresh fish to Tokyo markets and was making enough to support them. He had obtained a teaching position at Keiyo University for Genevieve.

Genevieve's heart was heavy as she told her children goodbye. They were as downcast as she.

"Miss Caulfield, we'll miss you so much," they told her. "Please come back again soon."

Long after she was on her way, Genevieve remembered their voices with a feeling of homesickness. Yes, she would miss them too. But another duty called her now, a duty to a nation where she had spent almost

Yes, she would miss them too.

fourteen years and had made many fine friends. They had met with disaster and suffering and it was her turn to give back all the love, understanding, and helpfulness she had received from them in the past.

In so many ways it was not a happy homecoming, though old friends came eagerly to visit her in the suburbs where Nobu had found a place for his family to live. Among the first were the Sugis. Others she would never see again. Some were in prisons waiting to be tried as war criminals.

Tokyo itself was a wasteland, for the incendiary bombs had created conflagrations as monstrous as those which had swept the city after the great earthquake. Of the sea of homes which had once covered this plain, only a few fragments of stone steps leading to nowhere remained, some gaunt chimneys and charred leafless trees standing foolishly alone. Reconstruction was going forward slowly, because the long war had drained the country of food and people were starving and apathetic.

Japan had lost more than whole cities in the war. She had lost her past as well, a past which never before had known the heel of the invader. Now all was gone—even the myth of the emperor's divinity. In the years to come she would have to seek out new values, new codes of living to get back her vitality.

"And not just Japan," Genevieve told herself. "Everywhere people had better start looking to their values or the whole world will be reduced to the dimensions of Tokyo today."

In October Nobu and Mary were married. As she sat in church listening to the beautiful nuptial Mass, Genevieve remembered another wedding in Bangkok. Then the air had been heavy with the spring odors of frangipani and jasmine. Now the Japanese maple trees were lifting the great flaming torches of fall against a brilliant blue sky. Then she had had the joy of seeing her daughter Haruko united with a fine young man. Now she had the satisfaction of seeing the little family which Haruko had left behind complete again in God. Her responsibility was over and her mind could rest easy at last.

On August 6, 1949, Genevieve was invited by the mayor of Hiroshima to attend the ceremony which the city held yearly to commemorate the dropping of the first atomic bomb.

In prewar days Hiroshima had been a charming little town dreaming its life away upon the delta of the Ota River which multiplies here to reach the ocean in seven meandering streams. During the war, however, it had reverted to the role it had played intermittently throughout history—that of a military center. Despite this it had been little troubled by air raids, and the population of some three hundred thousand had been congratulating one another on their immunity.

Then, on that August 6, a high-flying plane had dropped a single parcel which came down gradually by parachute. In mid-air it exploded with a flash of unearthly, searing light. Four square miles of city were obliterated by that single blast. Some hundred thousand people were killed outright by it and the fires it started. Others died later of the lingering illness it caused, while many of those who survived were left with badly scarred and maimed bodies and weakened health.

During her visit in 1949, Genevieve talked to some of these victims—the blinded, the maimed, the disfigured—and everyone of them explained to her earnestly the mission to which their lives were now dedicated.

"We live and work and pray for the banishment of war," they told her, "because, now that man has the atomic bomb, international peace is the world's only hope."

It *is* our only hope, Genevieve thought. Once again, touched beyond tears by the earnest voices of Hiroshima, she rededicated her life to the ideal that had first brought her to the Orient. She, too, by word, by deed, by prayer, would do all in her power to bring home to men their universal brotherhood. For now that airplanes had shrunk oceans to millponds and whole continents to meadowlands, now that a single small bomb could wipe out a city in a flash of blinding light, men could no longer afford to be foreigners one to another.

"If there are any foreigners left now," Genevieve told herself, "they must live on Mars or Venus or some other planet. Here on Earth, whether we like it or not, we have each and everyone of us become our brother's keeper."

CHAPTER **12**

THE AWARD

December 6, 1963. It was a beautiful day to receive an award, Genevieve thought as her car turned in through the gate that opened on the White House grounds. There was a nip to the air, but the sunshine was warm and pleasant. A light, inquiring breeze was blowing. Genevieve felt it cool against her cheek.

It should have been a happy time for the men and

women who with Genevieve were gathering here. Though they came from many walks of life and from distant parts of the world they all had one thing in common. They had been summoned to Washington, D.C., by President Kennedy to be awarded the Presidential Medal of Freedom.

But there was sadness in that company because the idealistic young man who had selected them for this great honor would not be there to hand out the awards. He had been assassinated on the streets of Dallas just two weeks before. The whole nation was in mourning. The mantelpiece of the State Dining Room where the ceremonies were to be held was draped in black.

Solemnly the men and women filed into that room. With them were other important visitors, members of the Supreme Court, the Cabinet and Congress. Genevieve couldn't help thinking of those days years ago when she had lived in this city and attended Trinity College to make a dream come true. Who would have believed then that the dream at last would lead her, an honored guest, into such distinguished company.

Genevieve seated herself and as she did so a picture flashed through her mind. It was the picture of Mary and Nobu and their family, five children in all now, counting the twins. What a to-do of compliments there had been when Genevieve had told them of her award. But Nobu had capped it all by saying, "If I had had any medals to give, you would have had them long ago,

Mother. Whatever would have happened to me and the twins without you?"

Much of good had happened to Nobu since the war. His little fish business had been transformed into a flourishing import-export company. But then the whole of Japan like Nobu's business was flourishing. Japan and America were now closer in friendship than they ever had been before. Genevieve's work there had long since been over. Bangkok had drawn her back again with its needs.

Bangkok like Tokyo was being shoved forward into the modern era. More and more canals were being filled up and new roads laid out to take care of the congested traffic problems. Automobiles of all makes were speeding, honking, weaving their way through the narrow streets. Yet Genevieve's former pupils, some with canes, others without, were able to negotiate those streets about as easily as the sighted.

One by one they passed gaily through Genevieve's mind. How joyously they had all worked to prove their value as individuals. And how well they had succeeded. Every one of them was earning a comfortable living. Some were even married and had children.

And what an example they had set. The people of Thailand had caught the message and taken the school to its heart. It would never have to put up with makeshift quarters again. Now it was housed in new buildings with enlarged classroom space and sunny, comfortable dormitories. The government contributed one-sixth of the necessary funds to keep the establishment running. And generous donations from all over the country made up the rest.

Just in the last few years Genevieve's adopted daughter, Aurora Lee, had gone to Chiengmai to open a school for the blind in the mountain town where Genevieve and Miss Vedhi had traveled years before to recruit pupils.

Aurora, little Knitting, the waif from the Chinese slums whom Genevieve and Haruko had rescued from a lingering death, had grown into a young woman with the same integrity of purpose, the same warm, earnest heart she had shown as a child. Genevieve had sent her to Overbrook on a scholarship for four years, and afterwards she had come back to teach at the school.

Aurora wasn't alone now though. She had a little girl to love and keep her company, making Genevieve a grandmother all over again. Aurora had adopted the little girl from a family who was going to sell her because they thought she was bringing them bad luck. Aurora had named her Rose Angela, but she called her Rosebud.

Rosebud was six years old now. On Genevieve's last visit, she had shyly pressed a scarf into her hands.

"It's a gift for you, Grandma," she said proudly. "I made it."

Now, sitting among the distinguished company in

the White House, Genevieve recalled again with a smile the feel of that shoddy knitted scarf into which the child had poured long hours of tedious, loving work.

How beautiful, Genevieve thought softly to herself, remembering another little girl of long ago whose hands had moved so slowly in a despised work.

Knitting—its warm and homely skeins had run like a theme throughout her life. In fact that life was like a piece of knitting held together by the innumerable stitches of daily deeds.

Nothing was ever finished, really, because as soon as one thing was well on the way another popped up that had to be tended to. The School for the Blind was established. And the Thais had even opened a school for the deaf in Bangkok. But there were the crippled children who needed help. Genevieve had become an active charter member of the Foundation for the Rehabilitation of the Crippled which was organized by public-spirited Thais, and had put her whole heart into the work as before she had for the blind.

In the middle of this had come an invitation from Vietnam to help the blind children of that country. Genevieve had gone at once and opened a school in Saigon. Then she had begun organizing another school to train teachers to work with the blind children in the provinces. But of course the adult blind of Vietnam needed help too, and after that came the crippled children there.

"Whatever thy hand findeth to do, do it with all thy might," was Genevieve's motto, and it seemed that everywhere she looked she could always find something more to do, not big things or noble ones or even outstanding ones so far as she could see. Just things to be done by someone and she was there. That was why she was so amazed the day she received a telegram from the Ramon Magsaysay Foundation in the Philippines.

The Foundation, which is patterned upon the Nobel Prize Foundation of the West, was established to honor the memory of Ramon Magsaysay, the Philippine Islands' great president who had been killed in an airplane crash in 1957. Since 1958 it has been presenting five yearly awards for outstanding achievements in various fields in the Far East. With each award comes a gift of ten thousand dollars.

"Miss Genevieve Caulfield," the telegram read, "this is to inform you that the Magsaysay Foundation has selected you to receive the annual Magsaysay award for International Understanding."

It was the highest award the Far East could give.

Now Genevieve was about to receive the highest civilian award her own country could bestow. President Johnson had taken his place before the mantel. His speech was short and poignant. His grief-stricken voice dropped each word tellingly into the quiet room.

". . . there is little we do not now know of evil, but it is time to turn once more to the pursuits of honor and excellence and of achievement that have always marked the true direction of the American people. . . . I want particularly to thank you for reminding us that whatever evil moments may pass by, we are and we shall continue to be a people touched with greatness, called by high destiny to serve great purposes."

Up went Genevieve's head at those words. Yes, it was the voice of destiny alone that could have inspired the young girl of long ago to smash against obstacle after obstacle to accomplish the work that was hers to do. And now the fulfillment of that work was being expressed in the words of the simple citation with which President Johnson was awarding her the medal:

"Genevieve Caulfield—Teacher and humanitarian, she has been for four decades a one-woman peace corps in Southeast Asia, winning victories over darkness by helping the blind to become full members of society."

Once again Genevieve was embarking for Europe, but not in a boat as she had years before with Haruko. Times had changed. Now it was to be a fast jet plane that was to carry her to Italy for a few pleasant holidays in Rome before flying on to Bangkok and South Vietnam and the work that still waited her there.

All the same there were similarities between the two leave-takings. On this occasion, as on that other years before, friends had come to counsel her gravely.

"Stop and think it over, Genevieve. You've done your

share in life. Take the rest and security here at home that you've earned."

"Security," Genevieve had answered. "Who is really secure for one single minute. We are secure only in the love of God. And there's so much to be done in this blessed world."

And now the last goodbye was said. The plane was lifting over the runway, gaining altitude, streaming eastward, cutting the blue sky like a bright, silver flame. The vibrant rhythms of the great metal bird, as always, filled Genevieve with a sense of adventure and anticipation.

Stay at home? Retire? Genevieve would never dream of retiring as long as a single person had need of her. She would always be going on.

FOR MORE ABOUT GENEVIEVE CAULFIELD

Busch, Noel F. *Thailand.* Princeton, New Jersey: D. Van Nostrand Co., Inc., 1959.

————. *Two Minutes to Noon.* New York: Simon and Schuster, Inc., 1962.

Caulfield, Genevieve. *The Kingdom Within.* Edited by Ed Fitzgerald. New York: Harper & Brothers, 1960.

Hersey, John. *Hiroshima.* New York: Bantam Books, Inc., 1959.

Storry, Richard. *A History of Modern Japan.* Harmondsworth, Middlesex, England: Penguin Books, Ltd., 1961.

INDEX

THE AUTHOR AND HER BOOK

MARGARET RAU *was born in Swatow, China, and lived there for most of the first eleven years of her life. She first learned to speak Chinese and then later English. After graduating from high school in America, she returned to China for two years and studied the language, literature, and history of the country. She later attended the University of Redlands, California, and also received credits from Columbia University and the University of Chicago. Mrs. Rau wrote a children's adventure novel,* The Band of the Red Hand *(Alfred Knopf, 1938), from her knowledge of China and collaborated with her husband and Charles Chaplin, Jr., on* My Father: Charlie Chaplin *(Random House, 1960). She and her husband, Neil, reside in Los Angeles, California, and are the parents of five children. In addition, they have adopted two little girls in the Orient, one in Japan, the other in Hong Kong.*

DAWN FROM THE WEST *(Hawthorn, 1964) was designed by Stefan Salter and completely manufactured by American Book—Stratford Press. The body type is Linotype Janson, based on the letters of Anton Janson, a Dutch punchcutter who worked between 1660 and 1687.*

A HAWTHORN BOOK

ABOUT CREDO BOOKS

CREDO BOOKS is an important new series of biographies that will appeal to both boys and girls. The subjects of these biographies are Catholics, but their stories are not of their faith so much as how that faith helped them to lead remarkable lives. Past and present will be represented here: a sculptor who left a priceless treasure of art to mankind, or a movie star who was an idol to young and old alike; the president of a South American country who fought against and lost his life to Communist terrorists. Heroes are made by the greatness of the human spirit and all the figures to be portrayed in CREDO BOOKS were great in spirit, courage and effort, no matter what task they took upon themselves.

The authors of these new books have been carefully chosen both for their ability to make biography come alive for young people and their knowledge of their subjects. Such authors as Terry Morris, Albert Orbaan, Donald Demarest, Gary Webster, Ruth Hume, Frank Kolars and Jack Steffan will be represented.

To give CREDO BOOKS the benefit of their knowledge and experience, an editorial board of distinguished representatives from the fields of education, librarianship and the Catholic Press, as well as Hawthorn's own editorial staff, choose both subject and author for each book in the series.

As an example of the variety of personalities in this series, you will find the following figures portrayed.